HandMade
in the Northern Forest

**A guide to fine art and craft traditions in
Maine, New Hampshire, Vermont and New York**

Published by the Northern Forest Center and
Businesses for the Northern Forest

**Northern
Forest
Center**

BUSINESSES
FOR THE
NORTHERN
FOREST

For book ordering information, see
www.HandmadeInTheNorthernForest.org
2006

Published by the Northern Forest Center and Businesses for the Northern Forest on behalf of *HandMade in the Northern Forest*, a collaborative effort to recognize and promote the fine art and craft traditions of the Northern Forest. Participating organizations include: Adirondack North Country Association, Appalachian Mountain Club, Women's Rural Entrepreneurial Network (New Hampshire), St. Lawrence County Arts Council (New York), Arts Alliance of Northern New Hampshire, Bethel Area Chamber of Commerce (Maine), Maine Highlands Guild, Maine WoodNet.

Published 2006

Book design by Nomad Communications, Inc.
Cover design by Kelly Short
Additional design and production by Karyn Smart
Printed by Penmor Lithographers
ISBN 0-9710504-1-4

HandMade
in the Northern Forest

A guide to fine art and craft traditions in
Maine, New Hampshire, Vermont and New York

Table of Contents

Acknowledgments

More than a dozen organizations across the Northern Forest of Maine, New Hampshire, Vermont, and New York collaborated to produce *HandMade in the Northern Forest: A guide to fine art and craft traditions in Maine, New Hampshire, Vermont and New York*. Inspired by the quality, character and value of the region's handmade products—and determined to support this growing and important segment of the region's rural economy—we have collected more than 300 businesses into this first-ever driving guide to the Northern Forest's arts and crafts venues. The Northern Forest Center and Business for the Northern Forest could never have published *HandMade* without the dedication of the project's steering committee, whose members helped to recruit businesses, develop the driving routes and offer advice throughout the project.

Adirondack North Country Association
Appalachian Mountain Club
Arts Alliance of Northern New Hampshire
Bethel Area Chamber of Commerce (Maine)
Maine Highlands Guild
Maine WoodNet
St. Lawrence Country Arts Council (New York)
Women's Rural Entrepreneurial Network (New Hampshire)

Special thanks are due to the following steering committee members who invested hours in developing the guidebook, sharing their contacts and reviewing the book throughout its production: Katy Curnyn, Nadia Korths, Chris Krauss, Hilary Oak, Frumie Selchin, Tracy Stutzman and Robin Zinchuck.

We owe a tremendous debt to Becky Anderson and the "HandMade in America" team in western North Carolina for providing motivation, guidance and the confidence that handmade traditions can provide an anchor to changing communities and economies in the Northern Forest region. Our guidebook is modeled on theirs, *The Craft Trails of Western North Carolina*, which is now in its third edition.

We are grateful to many others for their assistance, and offer special thanks to the Adirondack North Country Association and the Appalachian Mountain Club for securing and administering funding for the project.

Sincere thanks are due to the following for their financial support:

Great Bay Foundation
Maine Community Foundation
John Merck Fund
National Endowment for the Arts
New Hampshire State Council on the Arts
Northern New Hampshire Foundation
USDA Rural Development, New Hampshire
USDA Rural Development, New York
USDA Rural Development, Vermont

The staff of Businesses for the Northern Forest, including Kelly Ault, Richarda Ericson and Anna Downes, compiled and edited the hundreds of listings in *HandMade in the Northern Forest*, with help from Nadia Korths in New York and Amy Scott (and special assistance from Gail Scott) in Maine and New Hampshire. The Northern Forest Center's Mike Wilson wrote the narrative sections of the guidebook, and Kelly Short managed the editorial process and production. Mary Ellen MacCoy, Rebecca Brown and Shelly Angers provided invaluable editing on a lengthy manuscript.

Jill Harris helped launch *HandMade in the Northern Forest* as a venture in social entrepreneurism, and Terry Martino and Nadia Korths of the Adirondack North Country Association provided crucial project leadership in New York as well as valuable marketing and networking support to craft-based businesses.

Cathy Poppenwimer of the Appalachian Mountain Club produced all the maps in the book, carefully and cheerfully tracking down information about the most remote areas into which the guidebook will lead visitors.

Introduction

A kaleidoscope of color, form and texture, the handmade art and crafts in this guide reveal the rich variety, skill, creativity and traditions of the Northern Forest of Maine, New Hampshire, Vermont, and New York.

The swirl of blue in a stained glass window reflects waves on Lake Champlain. The cedar ribs and planking of a wood-canvas canoe draw on generations-old memory of its birch-covered inspiration. Basket and blanket weavers lace black ash, sweet grass or handspun wool into intricate patterns and shapes. A potter finishes bowls with glazes tinted by the minerals from nearby soil. All this work, and more, expresses a powerful connection between people and the landscape in one of America's great forest regions.

The listings in this guide include studios, workshops, galleries, museums and markets that showcase handmade artwork from the region's folk and fine art traditions. Driving the back roads and byways of a place known for country stores, picturesque villages and vast forests, you'll find artists in their studios and craftspeople in their workshops creating one-of-a-kind pieces.

Watch as a blacksmith hammers the delicate wings of a dragonfly in iron, and you will see his connection to the world around him. When a wood-turner hollows and polishes a burled, gnarly stump into a graceful centerpiece, you will discover the intricate patterns beneath the bark's surface. Observing a basket maker pound strips from a black ash log to bend and weave into a sturdy vessel, you'll gain a new understanding of patience.

The Northern Forest has inspired and influenced creativity for generations. Let *HandMade in the Northern Forest* guide you along country roads to discover its hidden gems and hard-to-find places.

HandMade Traditions

For generations, artists and craftspeople have drawn upon the forests, farms, mountains, rivers and lakes of the Northern Forest as sources of inspiration and raw material for their work.

The design woven into a blanket in the Adirondacks reflects the same forest that inspires a quilt pattern in the White Mountains. A wood carver in Maine uses the same white pine as his counterpart in Vermont. Artists celebrate the slant of winter light across mountain valleys and the glow of autumn leaves. Basket-makers seek the increasingly rare brown ash trees to provide the raw material for sturdy, elegant baskets. The images, designs, and materials that find their way into fine and folk art across the region are part of a story told by people whose hands reach through generations of practice to create the work we find today.

While local and personal distinctions abound, the artists and craftspeople showcased here draw upon a shared natural and human heritage. Their work is an invitation to know the woodlands, mountains, waterways and people of the Northern Forest through the vision and insights of those who use their hands and heritage to shape a vibrant and evolving culture.

Let their stories and their craft draw you deeper into the Northern Forest.

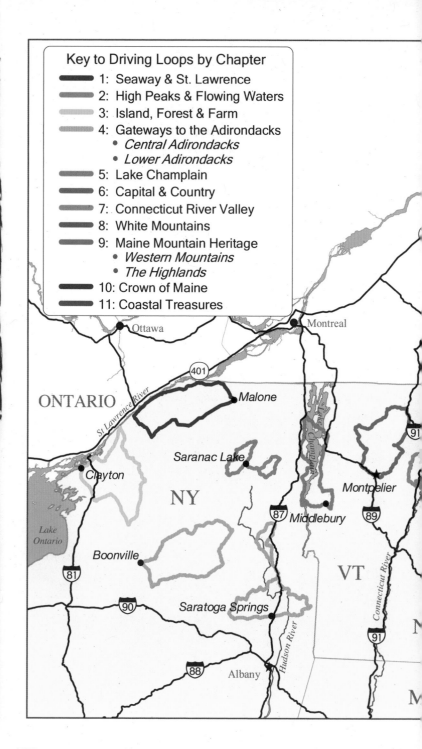

Key to Driving Loops by Chapter
1: Seaway & St. Lawrence
2: High Peaks & Flowing Waters
3: Island, Forest & Farm
4: Gateways to the Adirondacks
   • *Central Adirondacks*
   • *Lower Adirondacks*
5: Lake Champlain
6: Capital & Country
7: Connecticut River Valley
8: White Mountains
9: Maine Mountain Heritage
   • *Western Mountains*
   • *The Highlands*
10: Crown of Maine
11: Coastal Treasures

The Journey: How to use this guide

This guidebook describes 13 routes through the forests, farmlands, and rural communities of the Northern Forest. As outlined on the accompanying maps, each tour follows state highways and back roads through distinct landscapes. Chapter overviews offer glimpses of the journey ahead and some travel tips about distance and time to complete the tour. Numbered icons on the maps identify artists' galleries, studio workshops and craft marketplaces along each route. Each chapter features full descriptions of each craft business, as well as listings for selected special attractions, lodging and restaurants

Explore all or part of a route, starting and ending wherever you like. Routes vary in length and terrain. Some sections can be explored by bike or on foot. Others will take you to places from which you can venture deeper into the Northern Forest if you're up for an outdoor adventure. Whatever your pace, the listings in this guide can serve as inspiration and a point of departure—inviting you to take in the view and see what lies just beyond the bend.

Maps & Navigation

The maps included in this guide are intended to provide basic guidance to help you find studios, workshops and retail spaces featuring handmade art and crafts of the Northern Forest. The scale of the maps, however, imposes limitations. We strongly suggest that you take along a high quality local map or gazetteer to aid in navigation. For the sake of clarity, we have not shown all roads on these maps— just those important for navigating the routes presented. Marked distances should be generally accurate to within a half mile, but be sure to keep a close eye out for business signs along the way.

Icons on each map indicate the locations of businesses along main roads and in villages. For listings located farther off the beaten path, we have included driving directions at the end of the listing. The maps indicate excursions or side trips with a lighter shaded line; be sure to read the driving notes if you head off on one of these side trips.

Most businesses are well marked, but a few are in residential areas. In such cases, look for the address number on the mailbox, or call ahead or check websites for detailed directions.

The driving loops featured in the guidebook range from about 100 miles to nearly 300 miles. The tours follow local roads and state highways rather than Interstates, so expect speed limits of 50 mph and below, as well as traffic lights, stop signs and pedestrians.

If you've got the time, some of the loops can best be enjoyed over a 2- or 3-day span, giving you ample time to investigate the studios and galleries and enjoy the scenery and hospitality. On the other hand, if time is short, concentrate your exploration by picking a destination with a cluster of artisans and crafts people.

Icons & Categories

All listings are divided into six categories to give you a sense of what you can experience at each business. Keep in mind that the categories are general and you may find a wide array of creative work even within one category. Some businesses—such as an inn that serves meals, or a restaurant that features artwork—may be marked with more than one icon in the text, but only one icon will be numbered and used to locate the listing on the map.

 A **Studio Workshop** is the artist's workplace, and you will generally be able to see signs of the artistic process, sometimes catching them in the middle of creating something new. In most cases, the artist's work is also featured for sale.

 An **Artist Gallery** is a showroom rather than a studio, and may range from rustic to formal, large to small. Again, you can generally count on the artwork being for sale.

A **Craft Marketplace** features the works of more than one artist or craft person, and in most cases will offer the greatest range of work under one roof. Of the three categories for fine art and craft listings, these will feel the most like a retail shop.

 A **Restaurant** serves meals, but may also feature local artists' work for viewing or for sale. Be sure to check listings to see which meals are served, and note that some are seasonal.

 A **Lodging** provides a place to sleep en route. Many feature their own restaurants.

 A **Special Attraction** might be a local park with a waterfall, a museum or other institution featuring local history, culture or heritage.

Listing Criteria

The sites included in this guide were evaluated through an application and on-site visit and selected based on criteria established by the steering committee. The steering committee called on craft artists, business owners, state officials, network representatives and leaders of cultural organizations to help develop the criteria. With few exceptions, each listing in this guidebook:

- Is located within the Northern Forest
- Features at least 75% handmade fine or folk art from the Northern Forest
- Is safe and accessible to the public, and
- Is marked by signs clearly visible from the road.

Most of the businesses listed here maintain consistent business hours, however some artists are only able to open their studio or workshop by appointment. Detailed hours of operation are provided with each listing, and a handicapped accessibility symbol indicates which listings are fully accessible. Visitors who require special assistance should contact sites and facilities directly.

In selecting inns, bed & breakfasts, restaurants and cafes, we sought those that met at least one of the following criteria:

- Are locally owned and operated
- Art part of a farm network or cooperative
- Are situated in an historic or culturally important structure
- Offer a unique story about the community, or
- Display work by local artists

A Final Word

We have made every effort to ensure that addresses, phone numbers, business hours and other information are correct, but all information is subject to change. The partners, steering committee members and publisher assume no responsibility for the completeness or accuracy of the information.

While we have worked hard to identify and include a fair representation of the many fine and traditional artists and craftspeople of the Northern Forest, we realize that these 300-plus listings are just a sampling of the creative work in the region. Our hope is that this edition of *HandMade in the Northern Forest* will serve as a starting point for expanding this network.

Please visit HandMadeintheNorthernForest.org for more inform-ation and updates on the HandMade in the Northern Forest project.

Discover the Northern Forest

The Northern Forest is the largest intact ecosystem east of the Mississippi. It comprises some 30 million acres of northern Maine, New Hampshire, Vermont, and New York and blends into adjacent Canada. It is a landscape of boreal and northern hardwood forests, wetlands, lakes, rolling hills, and rugged mountains, yet it lies between densely populated areas to both south and north. Its ecological significance is well documented, including vast areas of wild forest, critical habitat, and the headwaters of the major rivers of the Northeast.

Equally important are the people, communities, and cultures of the region. The Northern Forest has been a source of subsistence, wealth, recreation, and renewal for centuries. The native land of the Iroquois and Algonquian peoples, the Northern Forest later became America's first great wilderness, the cradle of mountaineering and winter sports in the nation, and the birthplace of the modern paper industry. One and a half million people make their homes, communities, and livelihoods here today in the face of a rapidly changing economy.

Roads less traveled

Most of the roads in this guide are paved, but some are not. This is a rural, often remote, region and signs indicating frost heaves, narrow bridges, and moose-crossing zones should be taken seriously! To make sure you have a safe and enjoyable trip, please keep in mind a few travel tips:

- Respect signs, limits and conditions—watch for people in crosswalks in small towns, and always keep an eye out for wildlife.

- Pick up a local map—the maps in this guide are a reference for the routes outlined here and are designed only to help you orient yourself. You will be able to venture further into the communities and landscape of the Northern Forest with a more detailed map.

- Be aware that some road signs might be missing or moved, and watch the mileage markers on the routes to stay on course.

- Share the road—whether it's a moose, tractor, logging truck or cyclist, allow plenty of room.

- Fill up the tank—distances are long, and gas stations are sometimes few and far between. Keep your fuel supply well above empty.

Cell phones and internet access are common throughout the Northern Forest, but coverage can be intermittent. Ask when you make your reservation for accommodations about internet hook-up and cell phone reception if these are necessary.

Safe & Respectful Visiting

Every listing in this guide welcomes visitors. The listing is your invitation into the studios and workplaces of people who want to share their knowledge and their stories. As their guest, please recognize and be respectful of the difference between their enterprises and large, commercial businesses. Use your discretion and keep in mind:

Objects and equipment may be fragile or dangerous, and some areas may be off limits engage in new experiences while being mindful of their hosts' rules, values and property.

Sustaining the Northern Forest

The Northern Forest is a complex ecosystem that relies on its lakes, rivers, mountains, farms, forests and villages to thrive. Some of the communities you will pass through are little more than a cluster of houses and a tiny church. Others have grown over the years to accommodate seasonal visitors. You can be sure that the people you meet will do everything possible to help you find your way, enjoy your stay and come back for more. At the same time, this forest and these communities are fragile and rely on your protection to remain as pristine and open as you will find them. The principles of eco-tourism offer guidance to help maintain the health of the Northern Forest:

Minimize impact—wherever possible, park the car and bike, walk, hike, snowshoe or paddle to experience the full spectrum of color, sound and history to be found here.

Be aware of the environment—carry out whatever you carry in.

Contribute to the economic health of small communities by choosing to eat, sleep and shop in locally owned businesses.

Consider the cost to these communities of sprawl and unchecked development and help raise awareness of their effects on downtowns and small businesses.

Additional Resources

Maine
Maine Office of Tourism
(888) 624-6345
www.visitmaine.com/home.php

Maine Tourism Association
(207) 623-0363
www.mainetourism.com/

State of Maine website
www.maine.gov/portal/visiting/

New Hampshire
**New Hampshire Division
of Travel and Tourism
Development**
(603) 271-2665
www.visitnh.gov/

**White Mountains Attractions
Visitors Bureau**
(603) 271-2665
or (603) 745-8720
www.visitwhitemountains.com

**White Mountain National
Forest**
www.fs.fed.us/r9/white/

**Pinkham Notch Visitor
Center**
(603) 466-2721
www.outdoors.org/lodging/pnvc/
index.cfm

New York
**Adirondack Regional Tourism
Council**
adk.com/home/z-home.htm

Adirondacks.Com
(518) 891-3745
www.adirondacks.com/

Adirondack NET
www.adirondack.net/index.html

Vermont
**Vermont Department of
Tourism and Marketing**
(802) 828-3676
www.travel-vermont.com/

**Vermont Chamber of
Commerce**
(802) 223-3443
www.vtchamber.com/

*Most communities in the
Northern Forest are served by
a local or regional chamber of
commerce. Inquire locally for
information.*

Chapter

1

Seaway & St. Lawrence

Just as the massive St. Lawrence River serves as the inland gateway to the Great Lakes, let the Seaway & St. Lawrence Tour serve as your gateway to the fine arts and traditional crafts to be found along its broad valley.

This two-day tour begins in Potsdam, home of the local campus of the State University of New York system as well as several fine art and craft galleries. The anglers in your group might want to stop by Damon Rods to pick up a handcrafted fly rod to ply the waters of the rivers and streams you'll cross on your trip. Heading west from Potsdam, follow Route 11 into Canton where you can stroll along the Grasse River and visit the North Country Folkstore to purchase and learn about authentic North Country traditional arts and crafts.

As you travel northwest toward the St. Lawrence Seaway, watch for the horse-drawn buggies of Amish residents around Heuvelton and visit the Heritage Cheese House to sample fine cheeses made of milk from Amish dairies.

Canadian visitors may want to begin this tour in Ogdensburg, home of the nationally renowned Frederic Remington Art Museum. From here, your journey carries you northeast along the shores of the St. Lawrence. Enjoy the drive along the wide-shouldered road that parallels the river, crossing dozens of tributaries and offering views of islands and broad bays. In Hogansburg, stop at the Akwesasne Cultural Center to learn about the Mohawk Nation and the St. Regis Mohawk Reservation that straddles the New York, Quebec, and Ontario borders. While you're there, pick up handcrafted items bearing the Tree of Peace—symbol of the Iroquois Confederacy.

Follow the Salmon River south to Malone where you'll cross the Salmon River Gorge, visit a fine art gallery and test the comfort of carefully crafted Adirondack furniture before heading west to complete the loop in Potsdam.

From the foothills of the Adirondacks to the shores of the St. Lawrence River, relax and enjoy the quiet culture of the Seaway & St. Lawrence Tour.

Photo by: Carl Heilman II

Cultural Heritage Profile

Preserving Traditional Arts in Upstate New York

Northern Forest craft traditions have arisen from generations of people using local resources to make comfortable lives in the face of a challenging northern climate and a remote landscape. Most often valued today for their aesthetic form, folk and traditional arts are typically rooted in function. For example:

- Sturdy pack baskets allowed hunters and trappers to carry supplies into the forest before the advent of modern backpacks;

- Braided and hooked rugs protected feet from cold floors on wintry nights;

- Quilts transformed scraps of old cloth into warm bed covers;

- Carved wooden decoys were used to draw ducks within range of hunters;

- Carefully crafted guide boats and canoes provided a practical means of long-distance travel along the region's lakes and rivers.

Since 1986, Traditional Arts in Upstate New York (TAUNY) has worked to preserve and support these and other traditional arts in New York's 14-county North Country. For TAUNY, and other folklife organizations, traditional and folk arts are distinct from formal arts in that they are typically distinct to a particular group of people, are usually several generations old, and are passed informally from one generation to the next. Traditional arts are not taught in classrooms.

Over the years, TAUNY's offerings have grown to include an extensive archive of interviews and recordings of local folk artists; workshops by traditional craftspeople and musicians; a series of exhibits, publications, recordings, and radio productions; and a

register of "Very Special Places." TAUNY's North Country Heritage Awards have recognized more than 40 outstanding folk and traditional artists.

As part of your trip on the Seaway and St. Lawrence Tour, stop by TAUNY's North Country Folkstore in Canton (see page 11) to learn about and purchase some of the best examples of authentic folk and traditional arts of the Northern Forest.

Seaway &
St. Lawrence

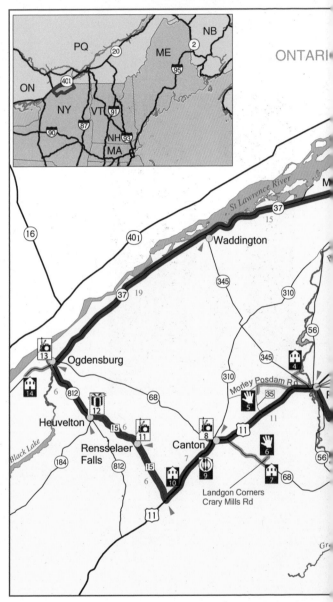

The main portion of the Seaway & St. Lawren

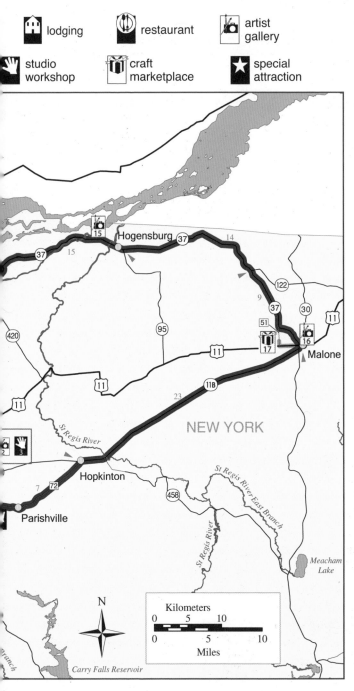

🏠 lodging	🍴 restaurant	📷 artist gallery
✋ studio workshop	🎁 craft marketplace	★ special attraction

p is approximately 150 miles long.

POTSDAM

Clarkson Inn

This two-story Victorian building greets visitors as they arrive in the village of Potsdam with an understated elegance blending with the historic downtown. The Inn has 40 deluxe rooms complete with modern connections and is walking distance to restaurants and shops.

800-790-6970 • 315-265-3050
One Main St., Potsdam, NY • www.clarksoninn.com

Creative Spirit Art Center

Expect the unexpected in this colorful collection of art and fine crafts by more than 150 artists from the region. Visitors will find three galleries with changing exhibits as well as quality collections of jewelry, pottery, baskets, clothing, woodwork, weaving, photography, art glass, toys, quilts, furniture, paintings, prints, and cards. Two classrooms are used for art and craft classes.

Open year round. Monday–Thursday 9 am–5 pm, Friday & Saturday 9 am–6 pm, Sunday 12 noon–4 pm.

315-265-3949
6 Raymond St.,
Potsdam, NY
www.spiritofcreativity.com

Creative Spirit Art Center

 lodging   restaurant   artist gallery

Frederic Remington Art Museum

The Northern Forest may seem an odd place to find art works that shaped the image of the American West—but it's actually one of the best.

Born in Canton, New York, Frederic Remington found his calling illustrating scenes from the western frontier during the late 19th century. After traveling widely and sketching the people and places he witnessed, he moved back east and established himself as an illustrator of western scenes for magazines including Harper's Weekly, Harper's Monthly, Collier's, Boys' Life, *and* Cosmopolitan. *Best known for his illustrations, Remington also was an accomplished sculptor and painter of western settlers, cowboys, and Native Americans facing the struggles of the frontier.*

Today, many of his works, as well as diaries, tools, and letters, are on display at the Frederic Remington Art Museum in Ogdensburg. Stop by for a view of the works that continue to influence the mythic image of America.

Damon Rods

Reel one in with a handmade fishing rod and rod components. This studio specializes in unique fly-fishing rods, each one individually evaluated and tested to ensure maximum performance. All phases of rod evaluation, assembly, adjustment and finishing are performed by a single rodcrafter from start to finish.

Open year-round.

315-265-0174 • 19 Market St., Potsdam, NY
www.damonrods.com

Arts Central—The St. Lawrence County Arts Council

The St. Lawrence County Arts Council's gift shop and gallery features art in all forms by regional artists, including music and books. Relax in our arts resource area and learn about local artists and cultural events. Arts Central offers classes, family activities, an artists' studio tour, concerts in the park, outdoor art shows, a newsletter and a free SLC Arts Directory.

 studio workshop    craft marketplace   special attraction

Open Wednesday–Friday 10 am to 6 pm, Saturday 10 am to 4 pm. Open evenings and additional hours for classes, events, appointments, or whims!

315-265-6860 • 51 Market Street, Potsdam, NY
slcartscouncil@yahoo.com • www.slcartscouncil.org

Located on the second block of Market Street, in downtown Potsdam. Take Rt. 11 or 11B or Rt. 56 to Market Street. (Not shown on map.)

Raquette River B&B

This bed and breakfast offers the comforts of home, the hospitality of good friends, and a backdrop of scenic serenity. Visitors can spend the evening relaxing by the fireplace in the large living room and in the morning enjoy breakfast and a colorful sunrise over one of northern New York's most beautiful rivers.

Open year-round.

315-265-4104 • 408 River Road, Potsdam, NY
www.raquetteriverbedandbreakfast.com

Downtown Potsdam on first block of Market Street.

Black Dog Furniture

In a hay barn on a country road, Dennis Del Rossi produces rustic furniture by linking Adirondack tradition and contemporary craft. He uses local materials—mostly white cedar, but also cherry and birch—in crafting accessory pieces to dressers, armoires, and end tables.

Open year-round. Call for appointment.

315-386-2774 • 512 Finnegan Road, Potsdam, NY
adrddr@northnet.org

From Route 11 in Canton, take Route 310 north approximately 2 miles. Make right on to Finnegan Road. Barn workshop is approximately 3 miles on the right.

Encompassing some 2,800 square miles, St. Lawrence is the largest county in the state of New York.

Tidbits

 lodging   restaurant   artist gallery

Crary Mills Pottery

Ronald Larsen's pottery is intended for use, not contemplation—meant to inform the daily rituals of life with the tactile and visual qualities of handmade work. His pottery is individually hand thrown and assembled from various stoneware clay bodies.

Open year-round by chance or appointment.

315-386-4721 • 174 County Route 35, Canton, NY

From the village of Canton, follow NY 68 southeast about 4 miles to the crossroads of Langdon Corners. Turn left (northeast) onto Crary Mills-Eben Road (County Route 35). Proceed 0.8 miles to the pottery, which is located on the right at the Post Road Corner. Studio entrance at the rear.

Misty Meadows B&B

Take a break in this modern hall colonial, where Peter and Marcia Syrett make guests feel right at home.

315-379-1536 • 1609 State Hwy 68, Canton, NY
www.mistymeadowsny.com

On Rt. 68 between Langdon's Corners and Canton

Traditional Arts in Upstate New York (TAUNY)/North Country Center and Folkstore

Dedicated to documenting and presenting the traditional arts, artists and local culture of the North Country, TAUNY (Traditional Arts in Upstate New York) is a nonprofit regional arts organization.

North Country fiddler, painted woodcarving by Ron Riley, Massena, NY

 studio workshop

 craft marketplace

 special attraction

11

This Center houses changing exhibits and a permanent photo gallery of master storytellers, musicians, craftspersons, and community groups. The store features authentic, handmade products from individuals and families throughout the region, such as Mohawk sweetgrass baskets, Old Order Amish quilts, woodcarvings, woven and braided rugs, local food products, as well as recordings and publications about local life. The Top Shelf Collection offers collectors and connoisseurs unique pieces from master artists in limited supply.

Open Tuesday–Saturday 10 am–4 pm.
Closed Saturdays, July & August.
315-386-4289 • 2 W. Main St., Canton, NY • www.tauny.org

Return to Rt. 11 and travel south to the village of Canton. Store is on the right just after the bridge.

McCarthy's Restaurant and Harvest House Gifts

Known for the homemade desserts, breads and rolls made in the bake shop, the restaurant's menu has a accent serving blackberries, rhubarb, and 100% maple syrup. Downstairs, the gift shop has a country warm feeling using local antiques for displays and offering a selection of candles, linens, wreaths, and cards from local crafters and artists.

Restaurant: daily 7 am–9 pm. Gift shop: Monday–Saturday 9 am–7:30 pm, Sunday 10 am–3 pm. Restaurant is handicapped accessible. Gift shop is not handicapped accessible.

315-386-2564 (restaurant)
315-386-4010 (gift shop)
5821 US Highway #11,
Canton, NY
www.harvesthousegifts.com

Follow Rt. 11 south toward DeKalb, about 1 mile south Canton.

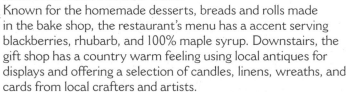

 lodging   restaurant artist gallery

White Pillars Lodging

Three adjacent buildings, all with sweeping views of 160 acres of woods and meadows, offer unique lodging options. The Homestead, an elegant Civil War vintage home, is a traditional bed and breakfast. The Craftsman Suites building is a turn of the century home restored to its original Mission Oak beauty, with luxurious additions of in-room fireplaces and Jacuzzis. The Amish Country Inn is a new building constructed by local Amish craftsmen, comprised of four small apartments suited for long-term stays.

Open daily.

315-386-2353 · 395 Old State Road, Canton, NY
www.whitepillars.com

From downtown Canton: Route 11 South turns right at 3rd traffic light. Follow highway 5 miles, turn right onto Lincoln Road, go 1/4 mile. Turn left onto Old State Road. White Pillars is 3/4 mile on right.

River House Wares & Restoration/ Ladies First, Gallery of Art

Housed in the restored Morrison Grist Mill along the Oswegatchie River, this eclectic gallery mixes history with vision. Visitors can find displays of

Morrison Mill

 studio workshop

 craft marketplace

 special attraction

Amish Traditions

As you drive the back roads of St. Lawrence County, you will likely encounter the horse-drawn black buggies of the local Amish residents who moved to the area in the mid-1970s in search of good and available farmland.

While their lives remain rooted in agriculture, local Amish supplement their incomes through a variety of cottage manufacturing and retail endeavors. In communities like Heuvelton, Depeyester, and Norfolk, watch for Amish farm stands selling maple syrup, fresh produce, baked goods, and hand-made quilts and aprons. You are welcome to stop to talk and purchase products, but please do not take pictures, as it violates Amish religious beliefs. Also, remember that the Amish do no business on Sundays.

architectural restoration pieces made in the county, raku and earthenware pottery, and environmental sculptures made by artist Kyle David Hartman.

Open daily by chance or appointment.

315-344-8882 · 315-344-7247 (cell)
317 Front St., Rensselaer Falls, NY · khartman@northnet.org
www.northnet.org/ghetto.studios

In Rensselaer Falls, turn right on Front Street. Gallery is on the left.

Heritage Cheese House, Ltd.

Sample this wonderful cheese manufactured by hand using Amish can milk as a mild source. Furniture, quilts, aprons, jams, and syrup made by Amish farmers can be found in this country store.

Open Monday–Friday 8 am–5 pm, Saturday 8 am–6 pm.

315-344-2216 · 4775 State Hwy. 812, Heuvelton, NY
www.heritagecheese.com

From Rennselaer Falls, take Front Street to Rt. 812 and turn right, store is on left.

 lodging   restaurant   artist gallery

Frederic Remington Art Museum

This Museum is dedicated to collecting, exhibiting, preserving and interpreting the art and archives of Frederic Remington. The collection includes a full spectrum of the artist's work, including some of his earliest achievements, many published paintings and drawings, and an inspiring variety of late-life paintings, which focus on the landscape.

Boat House at Ingleneuk, by Frederic Remington, ca. 1903-1907, oil on academy board, 12"x18" gift of the Remington Estate

Open May 1–October 31: Monday–Saturday 10 am–5 pm, Sunday 1 pm–5 pm. November 1–April 30: Wednesday–Saturday 11 am–5 pm, Sunday 1 pm–5 pm.
315-393-2425 • 303 Washington St., Ogdensburg, NY
www.fredericremington.org
Continue north on Rt. 812 to State Street in Ogdensburg and follow signs to museum.

Gran-View Quality Inn

Since opening in 1945, this hotel with a spectacular view overlooking the St Lawrence River, has been a destination for travelers by road or by water. Guests can relax and enjoy the comfortable guest rooms, fine dining, pool—even shuffleboard! The restaurant's philosophy—Food for Particular People— reflects the use of only the freshest products and combined with care and finesse, results in a memorable meal.

315-393-4550 • 800-392-4550
6765 State Highway 37, Ogdensburg
granview@1000islands.com

 studio workshop

 craft marketplace

 special attraction

15

Akwesasne Cultural Center, Inc./ Akwesasne Museum

Located in the community of Akwesasne, the Center's mission focuses on the interpretation of Akwesasne Mohawk culture. Permanent and temporary exhibitions of objects made by Mohawk people including paintings, drawings, beadwork, pottery, silverwork, cornhusk dolls, cradleboards—and most characteristic—black ash splint and sweetgrass baskets. Mohawk traditional arts use natural materials to portray culture, develop symbolism, stimulate economic development, and express identity. The Museum Shop carries handmade items representative of the collection.

Open Monday–Friday 8:30 am–3:30 pm.
$2 Adults, $1 ages 5–15, under age 5 free.
518-358-2461 • 321 State Route 37, Hogansburg, NY
www.akwesasneculture.org

Follow Rt. 37 north past Massena, 8 miles past the St. Lawrence Center Mall.

For ARTSake

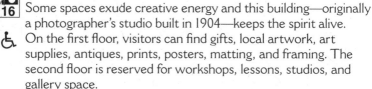

Some spaces exude creative energy and this building—originally a photographer's studio built in 1904—keeps the spirit alive. On the first floor, visitors can find gifts, local artwork, art supplies, antiques, prints, posters, matting, and framing. The second floor is reserved for workshops, lessons, studios, and gallery space.

Open Tuesday–Friday 10 am–5 pm, Saturday 10 am–4 pm.
518-483-9411 • 393 W. Main St., Malone, NY
www.forartsake.net

Adirondack Wood Furnishings

Surround yourself with the comfort of carefully crafted Adirondack furniture. At this store, find a full line of hand-sanded, solid, white pine furniture with contoured backs, seats, and traditional wide arms.

Open Monday–Friday 9 am–4 pm.
324 County Route 51, Malone, NY
www.adirondackwoodfurnishings.com

 lodging   restaurant   artist gallery

SunFeather Natural Soap Co. Inc

Luxury for the skin with over 100 varieties of handcrafted natural soap, candles, and bath and beauty products all made on site! Enjoy a tour of candle and soapmaking techniques using the time-honored kettle method. Learn about perfumery, aromatherapy, and the interesting story and philosophy behind this 26-year-old socially responsible enterprise. Locally made and internationally famous!

Open daily.

315-265-3648 · 1551 Hwy 72, Potsdam, NY· www.sunsoap.com

Continue west on Rt. 72, through Parishville Store is on the right.

St. Lawrence Open Studio Days

Just in time for the holidays!

Each November, the St. Lawrence County Arts Council presents its annual Artists' Studio Tour. For two days, local artists and craftspeople invite the public to visit their workshops and studios to discover insights to their creativity and purchase local works. The tour includes a terrific range of artwork and fine crafts, including work by ceramic and fiber artists, painters, wood workers, sculptors, basket makers, rug braiders, soap makers, glass blowers, and others.

Prior to the tour each year, complete brochures and studio maps are available free at local libraries, chambers of commerce, and craft galleries. Plans are in the works to start a summer studio tour. The SLC Arts Council also coordinates a variety of art-related classes and events throughout the year. To learn more, or to request a studio tour brochure or a free directory of area cultural resources, contact the St. Lawrence County Arts Council at (315) 265-6860 or (315) 393-7062; slcartscouncil@yahoo.com, or 51 Market St., Potsdam, NY 13676.

 studio workshop

 craft marketplace

★ special attraction

Chapter
2

High Peaks & Flowing Waters

To the east, the towering High Peaks of the Adirondack Mountains, including 5,344-foot Mount Marcy, lure hikers and climbers. To the west, an intricate web of lakes and rivers beckons paddlers and anglers. All along the way, artists and craftspeople invite you to share their reflections of this spectacular landscape.

Beginning in the All-American city of Saranac Lake, the High Peaks & Flowing Waters Tour traces a figure eight through some of New York's most striking scenery. Enjoy mountain

Photo by: Carl Heilman II

views to the east as you head north through Bloomingdale, to the windy road to Onchiota and a visit with Edith Urban and her unique collection of paintings and handmade teddy bears and quilts.

Stop for soft ice cream at Donnelly's and take a walk through the campus of Paul Smith's College on the shore of Lower St. Regis Lake before heading south past Lake Clear and Upper Saranac Lake and west to

Photo by: Jerry & Marcy Monkman/
EcoPhotography.com

Tupper Lake and Cranberry Lake. This really is lake country.

Returning to Saranac Lake, pause for a stroll on the walkway along Lake Flower and the Saranac River, then head east to bustling Lake Placid—home to the Adirondack Craft Center, boat makers, soap makers, galleries, and the sports complexes of the 1980 Winter Olympics. Continuing east, enjoy the views as you descend the pass to the villages of Keene and Keene Valley. Consider stopping for lunch with the locals at the Noon Mark Diner.

After a side trip to Elizabethtown, follow the Ausable River north to Upper Jay and Jay—towns on the sometimes forgotten side of the High Peaks where you'll find several craft galleries. In Wilmington, stop by The Corner Stone, a local women's artisan cooperative, and consider a drive to the top of Whiteface Mountain—site of the Olympic ski races in 1980.

The top of the mountain is the perfect spot to reflect on your discoveries along the High Peaks & Flowing Waters Tour.

Cultural Heritage Profile

Guides & Guide Boats

The wilderness guide has been a Northern Forest icon since the early 1800s. Nowhere did these men take on a more mythic status, though, than in the Adirondacks. There, wealthy "sports," as clients were called, would pay a high price to spend a week in the wilderness with legendary woodsmen. Some of the renowned guides included:

- Orson "Old Mountain" Phelps: a mountain guide believed to have cut the first trail to the summit of Mount Marcy—highest peak in the Adirondacks;

- Mitchell Sabattis: a Native American guide so respected that a mountain and a village were named for him after his death; and

- Alvah Dunning: the "Hermit guide of Racquet Lake," an acclaimed hunter, trapper, and angler, who once said of the sports he guided, "I kin git along without 'em. They're mostly durned fools, anyhow!"

The number of tourists seeking escape from the cities and adventure in the Adirondacks surged after the Civil War, and many native Adirondackers found opportunities to earn money guiding city folk into the mountains and along the waterways.

It was on the region's extensive waterways that the Adirondack Guide Boat also attained iconic status. Pointed at both ends like a canoe, the guide boat was propelled with oars like a rowboat—allowing the guide to transport his client and gear while leaving

A modern rendition of the venerable Adirondack Guideboat, made by Adirondack Guideboat, Inc. (see page 107).

the sport free to fish, watch for game, or just enjoy the scenery. While carrying capacity was an important characteristic, it was equally important that these craft be light enough for the guide to hoist onto his shoulders for the many carries between lakes and rivers.

Today, local guides and finely crafted guide boats remain important elements of Adirondack culture—and among the best ways to experience a genuine Adirondack wilderness experience.

High Peaks &
Flowing Waters

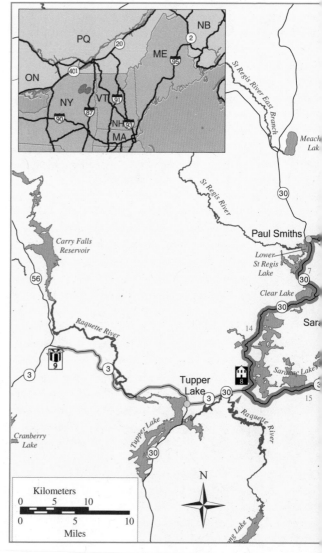

The main portion of the High Peaks & Flow

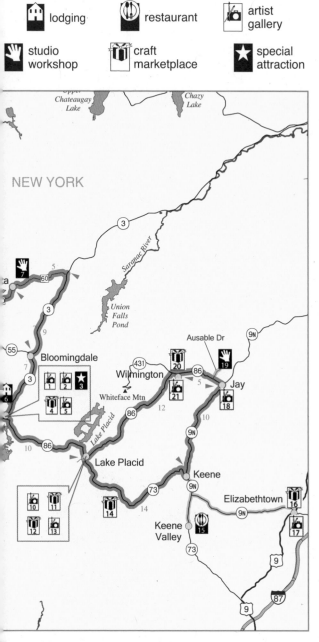

| | lodging | | restaurant | | artist gallery |
| | studio workshop | | craft marketplace | | special attraction |

...ater loop is approximately 117 miles long.

SARANAC

Adirondack Artists' Guild

Cooperatively owned, this inviting gallery features fine art by regional artists including paintings, photography, multi-media, sculpture, ceramics, and weaving.

Open Monday–Saturday 10 am–3 pm, Sunday, 12 noon–3 pm.

518-891-2615 • 52 Main St., Saranac Lake, NY
www.adirondackartistsguild.com

The Small Fortune Studio

Tim Fortune invites you into his working studio and gallery. His original oil and watercolor paintings and contemporary art focus on the Adirondack landscape. A second upstairs gallery presents contemporary works and photography.

Open Tuesday–Saturday 10 am–3 pm or by appointment.

518-891-1139 • 76 Main St., Saranac Lake, NY
www.fortunestudio.com

Sunset, Lower Saranac (oil painting)

🏠 lodding   restaurant   artist gallery

Paul Smith's Legacy of Hospitality

Just as the mid-1800s saw the Adirondacks emerge as a destination for adventure and respite in the wilderness, the era also saw the emergence of a hospitality tradition that continues today. Among the pioneers of this movement were Apollos A. (Paul) Smith and his wife, Lydia, who recognized an economic opportunity in providing luxury lodging in the heart of the remote forest. Though it was located sixty miles from the nearest railroad, the resort they built on Lower St. Regis Lake became synonymous with Adirondack hospitality. In the late 19th and early 20th centuries, Paul Smith's Hotel was a thriving resort destination for the rich and famous. Today Paul Smith's College continues the legacy of its namesake through its respected programs in culinary arts and hospitality, and the historic Hotel Saranac, which it owns and operates.

Third Thursday Gallery Walks

Every third Thursday of the summer months, galleries in downtown Saranac Lake open their doors for an evening of art! Meet artists, view a wide variety of pieces, meet with residents and visitors, and enjoy the pleasant summer weather in Saranac Lake.

Open June–September
4:30 pm–7 pm.

**Contact Small Fortune Studio,
518-891-1139
76 Main St.,
Saranac Lake, NY**

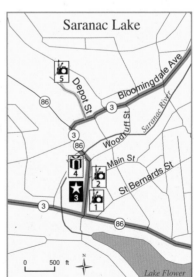

Saranac Lake

Lake Flower

 studio workshop

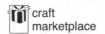 craft marketplace

 special attraction

25

Two Horse Trading Company

John and Carla own this shop of buckskin clothing, flint and steel, original artwork from Native American and historical reproduction artists, and decorative crafts related to spirituality. Native re-enactor John's warshirts are in private collections worldwide. Carla's original paintings and notecards reveal her fine art training.

Open Monday–Friday 10 am–6 pm, Saturday 10 am–5 pm, Sunday 11 am–3 pm. Winter: Tuesday–Saturday 10 am–5 p.m.
518-891-4055 • 24 Broadway, Saranac Lake, NY
carla@twohorsetrade.com

The Whistle Stop

Meet the artisans at this intimate cooperative gallery of crafts at the Union Depot, a restored historic train station. Handmade items include twig planters, candles, balsam pillows, porcupine quill jewelry, embroidered home decor and shirts, gift baskets, and pack baskets.

Open year-round. Summer and Fall train excursions leave for Lake Placid.
518-891-4759 • 42 Depot St., Saranac Lake, NY

The Doctor's Inn

This large, rambling Victorian was once home to the research doctors at the world famous Trudeau Sanatorium. The living room is warmed by a woodstove and surrounded by an eclectic collection of books. The wrap-around porch is reminiscent of the "cure" days and brings peacefulness to guests who enjoy the restorative powers of the fresh mountain air and carefree days.

Open daily.
518-891-3464 • 304 Trudeau Road, Saranac Lake, NY
www.docsinn.net

1.3 miles (3 km) from railroad crossing and look for sign to American Management Association. Take a sharp left to top of hill and see sign.

 lodging   restaurant   artist gallery

Edith Urban Gallery

Surrounded by beautiful gardens, Edith Urban creates "oil paintings in miniature and larger format, that realistically portray the landscape and wildlife of the Adirondacks." She also handcrafts fully jointed teddy bears with handmade clothing or accompanied by birds, rabbits or frogs. Visitors can find her quilts

of original design ranging from wall hangings to throws.

Open weekdays & Sunday 10 am–3 pm or by appointment.

518-891-5467
2305 County Route
60, Onchiota, NY
eurban@northnet.org

0.75 miles from Rt. 3.

St. Regis River

EXCURSION TO TUPPER LAKE AND CHILDWOLD

The Wawbeek on Upper Saranac Lake

Norman and Nancy Howard welcome visitors to this former private Great Camp on Upper Saranac Lake designed by William Coulter. Enjoy the self-guided nature trail on property or the naturalist guided tours in the summer. Both the bar and the dining room celebrate the Great Camp style with rustic furniture and exhibit works of the members of the Adirondack Artists Guild.

Open daily 8 am–8 pm.

518-359-2656 • 553 Hawk Ridge, Tupper Lake, NY
www.wawbeek.com

Located 1.5 miles north of the intersection of routes 3 and 30 between Saranac Lake and Tupper Lake.

 studio workshop

 craft marketplace

 special attraction

27

Leather Artisan

Revel in the texture of soft, supple leather at this shop. Over the last two decades, Donna and Tom Amoroso have traditionally crafted designer leather accessories that are meant to last, age, and gain in character. Visitors can also find items from other Adirondack crafters.

Open May–December: Monday–Saturday 10 am–6 pm, Sunday 12 noon–6 pm. January–March closed Tuesday and Wednesday.

518-359-3102 • Route 3, Childwold, NY
www.leatherartisan.com

12 miles to the west of Tupper Lake.

Adirondack Craft Center

Originally founded in 1986 as an outlet for Adirondack handcrafted products, today the Center represents over 300 local, regional and national artisans. The 4000-square foot facility features a marvelous collection of baskets, glass, jewelry, pottery, quilts, lamps, photography, sculpture, weaving, furniture, and ornaments.

Wooden loon by J.W. Daxbury (Dax' Dekes)

Open daily 10 am–5 pm.

518-523-2062 • 2114 Saranac Ave., Lake Placid, NY
www.adirondackcraftcenter.com

Located in Lake Placid Arts Center complex.

HEAD BACK THROUGH SARANAC LAKE TO LAKE PLACID

Good Things

Folks from far and near are following their nose to this shop of wonderful scents! The shelves are stocked with more than 200 bath & beauty products that are made by Sunfeather Natural Soap or on-site in the Good Things exhibition-style kitchen. Watch as Michelle makes her signature line of handmade glycerin soaps that are served to customers "by-the-slice."

Open daily 10 am–5 pm.

518-523-3015 • 18 Main Street, Route 86, Lake Placid, NY

 lodging   restaurant   artist gallery

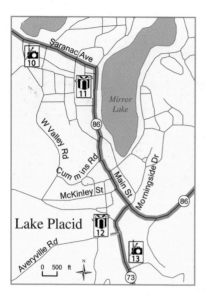

Placid Boatworks

This waterside shop features high quality solo and tandem recreational canoes, made of strong, lightweight carbon/Kevlar construction, with beautiful, hand-finished Adirondack cherry gunwales and seat frames. Be sure to stop by and see boat builders, Charlie and Joe. If the water's not frozen, visitors can enjoy a test ride out the shop's back door.

Open year-round.
518-524-2949 · 20 Averyville Road (just off Rt. 73), Lake Placid, NY · www.placidboats.com
Look for us on the left, across from the train station.

TWIGS

Accessories and furniture for the home, camp or cottage. This rustic gallery features work from eight artists and furniture makers. Framed oil paintings, prints, birch bark mirrors, desks, dressers, chairs, snowshoe lamps, clocks, giftware, and one-of-a-kind "woodsy goods." Look for the big twig chair.

Open daily
10:30 am–5:30 pm.
518-523-5361 · 121 Cascade Road (Route 73), Lake Placid, NY
twigsrus@westelcom.com

 studio workshop

 craft marketplace

 special attraction

29

South Meadow Farm Maple/Sugarworks
South Meadow Farm Lodge

Sweet sensations! This family-run maple sugaring operation makes the finest maple syrup and maple sugar candy around. Stay at this modern country-style bed & breakfast with beautiful views and watch the sap run!

Open year-round.

518-523-9369 • 67 Sugarworks Way, Lake Placid, NY

0.25 miles from Route 73, halfway between Lake Placid and Keene near Mt. Van Hoevenberg.

EXCURSION TO KEENE VALLEY AND ELIZABETHTOWN

Noon Mark Diner

Bring your appetite to this old-fashioned diner specializing in homemade food and friendly service. The fresh berry pies—with hand mixed and rolled crusts—are as tasty as they are memorable. Homemade breads make any meal a treat.

Open daily 6 am–9 pm.

518-576-9737 • 1770 NYS Route 73, Keene Valley, NY
www.noonmarkdiner.com

lodging   restaurant   artist gallery

Adirondack KK Ranch

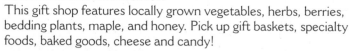

This gift shop features locally grown vegetables, herbs, berries, bedding plants, maple, and honey. Pick up gift baskets, specialty foods, baked goods, cheese and candy!

Open May–December: Monday–Friday 8:30 am–5:30 pm, Saturday–Sunday 10 am–4 pm. January–April: Monday–Friday 8:30 am–5:30 pm.

518-873-3209 · Court St. (Route 9), Elizabethtown, NY
adkkranch@yahoo.com

Healing Power

"To cure sometimes, to relieve often, to comfort always."

Edward Livingston Trudeau was just starting his physician's practice when he was diagnosed with pulmonary tuberculosis. A sportsman by nature, Trudeau chose a treatment of clean air and relaxation at Paul Smith's Hotel in the Adirondacks. Noticing good results, he moved his family to Saranac Lake in 1876, and established two important institutions. The Adirondack Cottage Sanitarium provided beds for pulmonary patients seeking treatment and an escape from the foul air of the cities. The second institution, the Saranac Laboratory for the Study of Tuberculosis, was the first tuberculosis research center in the nation.

Over time, Saranac Lake became famous as a place of healing, and it became common for residents to take in boarders seeking the "cure" of the fresh mountain air. Today, if you look closely at the older buildings in town, you will notice an unusual concentration of enclosed porches where patients sat to breathe their medicine.

 studio workshop

 craft marketplace

special attraction

Adirondack History Center Museum/Essex County Historical Society

The Museum displays artifacts from Essex County and the Central Adirondacks from the last two centuries. Ten major exhibit areas, in this three-story, neoclassical style, 1915 former school building, introduce visitors to early farming and frontier life, wilderness exploration and recreation, and transportation. Larger artifacts include an 1850s Washington printing press, 1887 Concord Stagecoach, 1920s stage curtain, bobsled from the 1932 Olympic Games, and a fire tower. The Colonial garden features plants and flowers patterned after the gardens of England and Williamsburg.

Open Memorial Day–Columbus Day:
Monday–Saturday 9 am–5 pm, Sunday 1 pm–5 pm.
518-873-6466 · 7590 Court Street, Elizabethtown, NY
www.adkhistorycenter.org

Jay Craft Center

Working in a restored Grange building on the village green for more than 25 years, Cheri Cross and Lee Kazanas make functional porcelain and stoneware pottery. In the gallery, visitors will find porcelain pots handpainted with Adirondack and floral themes as well as a delightful assortment of handcrafted toys, woodenware, jewelry, candles, photographs, and prints.

Open June–mid-October 10 am–5 pm.
Winter: Wednesday–Saturday, 10 am–5 pm.
518-946-7824 · On village green, Route 9N, Jay, NY
jaycraft@charter.net

Located 500 feet south of the intersection of Rt. 9N and Rt. 86.

 lodging restaurant artist gallery

Young's Studio & Gallery

This studio hosts some of the North Country's most talented craftspeople making pottery, etchings, woodwork, jewelry, and basketry. Terry's handmade paper books have won regional awards. Lucky visitors might catch Sue doing a raku firing!

800-842-1072 · 6588 Route 86, Jay, NY
www.youngsgallery.com

The Corner Stone

Serving as an artisan women's cooperative for the Whiteface Mountain region, visitors will find bug bonnets, stained glass, antler baskets, batik clothing, pottery, porcupine quill jewelry, and rustic furnishings.

Open daily, 10 am–5 pm.

518-946-1118 · 5698 Route 86 · Wilmington, NY
www.Adirondackhandmade.com

Capozio Gallery

Beaver, fox, mink, heron, osprey, and even an eagle are frequent visitors and inspire the work of Stevie Capozio, known for her Adirondack art and detailed enamels for over 30 years. Joe Capozio is an award-winning artist specializing in drawing and painting the figure.

Open May–October: Call for appointment.

518-946-2319
55 Riverbend Drive,
Wilmington, NY
www.capoziogallery.com
Off Route 86.

Ospreys in March

 studio workshop

 craft marketplace

 special attraction

33

Philosophers Camp

In the mid-1800s, the Adirondacks became a magnet for artists, philosophers, scientists and others seeking inspiration, perspective, and a mind-clearing experience in the wilderness. Among those drawn to the region was William Stillman of Cambridge, Massachusetts, who organized a month-long camping trip with a group of intellectuals on Follensby Pond in 1858. The group included Ralph Waldo Emerson whose poem "The Adirondacs" captured the sentiment of the scholars transported to the wilderness from their city homes.

> ... And, in the forest, delicate clerks, unbrowned,
> Sleep on the fragrant brush, as on down-beds.
> Up with the dawn, they fancied the light air
> That circled freshly in their forest dress
> Made them to boys again. Happier that they
> Slipped off their pack of duties, leagues behind,
> At the first mounting of the giant stairs....

The trip was further immortalized in Stillman's painting, The Philosopher's Camp, *currently among the holdings of the Concord Free Public Library in Massachusetts.*

 lodging   restaurant   artist gallery

Chapter

3

Island, Forest & Farm

Bounded by the Tug Hill Plateau, the St. Lawrence River, and the Adirondack Mountains, the landscapes and communities of the Island, Forest & Farm Tour are as diverse as the arts and handcrafts they inspire.

The two-day tour starts in Watertown, where winter winds from Lake Ontario meet the 2,000-foot Tug Hill Plateau to produce the heaviest snowfalls east of the Rocky Mountains. From Watertown head west under big skies through rolling farm country toward Clayton and the Thousand Islands region of the St. Lawrence where 1,700 islands have drawn summer people for rest, relaxation, and spiritual renewal for over 100 years.

Enjoy the view from the Thousand Island Bridge, as you cross over to Wellesley Island to explore the Northern Paradise Gift Shop and enjoy a bit of island ambiance. Crossing back to the mainland, head north to the arched gateway of Alexandria Bay—home to the Cornwall Brothers Store and the Heritage Arts Museum.

Heading inland to Redwood, consider stopping for the night at Sixberry Lake Campground in a cabin furnished with rustic furniture from nearby Creations in Wood. The spring-fed lake, sandy beach, and wooded shoreline provide an idyllic resting point.

After a short ride north to Hammond, cross the threshold into Yesteryear's Vintage Door Company and a showroom exhibiting the fine workmanship of solid custom crafted doors produced for customers from all across the country.

The second half of this tour brings you south through Gouverneur and into the fertile Black River Valley and the heart of New York's dairy and maple country. In Croghan, stop by the historic Croghan Meat Market before heading to the American Maple Museum for dessert. Further south in Lowville, visit the Lowville Producers Cheese Store to sample some of their 40 locally produced specialty cheeses.

Round out your trip with the fine crafts and spectacular views to be found along the northern edge of the Tug Hill Plateau.

From summer resorts to hard working farms, you'll find a wide range of community influences reflected in the art and craft work of the Island, Forest & Farm Tour.

Cultural Heritage Profile

Got Farms?

For the early Europeans who settled in the remote hills and valleys of the Northern Forest, farming and agriculture were necessary elements of life far removed from the conveniences of towns and cities. Over time, though, as more fertile land was cultivated in the Midwest and Great Plains, most of the farms that had been carved from the forest were abandoned for greener pastures.

While forestry and forest recreation shape the character of most of the Northern Forest today, here along the region's western edge, dairy farming and agriculture continue to dominate much of the local landscape and culture.

Nestled in the fertile Black River Valley between the Tug Hill Plateau and the Adirondack Mountains, Lewis County alone has

165,000 acres of agricultural land, and its dairy farms produce 500 million gallons of milk each year. With 53,000 head of cattle and only 26,700 people, the cows outnumber human residents nearly 2-1.

While a great deal of the milk produced in Lewis Country supplies the Kraft Cream Cheese factory in Lowville (the largest in the world), the 380 dairy farms in the county also supply more than 100 other agricultural businesses. Among these are a kosher milk plant and the Lowville Producers Cheese Store, where you can find more than 40 varieties including fresh-waxed cheddar wheels, Squeaky Fresh Cheese Curd, and XXX Treme 3 Year Old Cheddar.

In addition to the dairy products that dominate the local economy, the woodlots found on many farms supply timber for local crafts and wood products, as well as maple sap for syrup and sugar. Many enterprising farmers sell fresh produce directly from the backs of their trucks at local farm markets throughout the summer and early fall.

Photo by: John McKeith/EarthImagery

Island, Forest & Farm

The main portion of the Island, Fo...

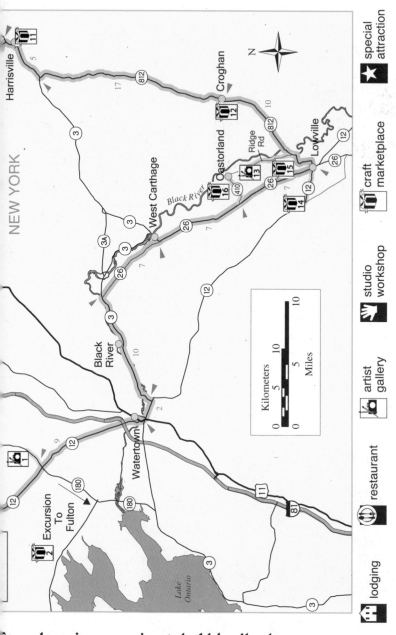

NEW YORK

Harrisville

Croghan

Castorland

West Carthage

Black River

Ridge Rd

Lowville

Black River

Watertown

Excursion To Fulton

Lake Ontario

N

Kilometers
0   5   10

0   5   10
Miles

special attraction

craft marketplace

studio workshop

artist gallery

restaurant

lodging

Farm loop is approximately 164 miles long.

EXCURSION OFF MAIN LOOP

🎦 Northern New York Agricultural
1 Historical Society Museum

At this Museum, the collecting, preserving and displaying of

historical materials relating to the farm and the farm home tell the story of the agriculture industry in northern New York. Also on location is a turn of the century Cheese Factory, built by a cooperative formed in 1886 as a means of creating a more marketable form of milk. The factory was in operation until the mid 1920s and produced Yankee and cheddar cheese.

Open daily June–September 9 am–3 pm. Closed Tuesday. $5 admission.

315-658-2353 • LaFargeville, Route 180, Stone Mills, NY
agstonemilles@usadatanet.net

EXCURSION TO FULTON: 90 MILES EACH WAY

🎁 The Wood Studio at Country Herbs & Flowers
2

Wood—harvested from the grounds in an environmentally friendly manner—is transformed with a scroll saw in as many

directions as a mind can wander. James Ireland makes and turns wooden items including clocks, crosses, butterflies, Christmas ornaments, jewelry, and bowls.

Open daily April–December 9 am–5 pm.

315-598-1343
963 County Route 8, Fulton, NY
waterlil@twcny.rr.com

 lodging   restaurant   artist gallery

Gold Cup Farms

Cheese making has been a tradition for well over a century in Jefferson County. Visitors to the old time general store will know why when they sample the "River Rat" cheddar. Other tasty treats from the region include pure maple syrup and Adirondack summer sausage.

Open daily 9 am–5 pm.

315-686-2480 • 242 James St., Clayton, NY
www.riverratcheese.com

Winged Bull Studio

Heritage and ingenuity come together in this 100-year old

Richardson Romanesque gallery with original fur beadboard interior. Greg Lago creates unique wood engravings from endgrain blocks of maple and cherry. The engraving is then printed on a antique letterpress to produce limited edition original prints in the late 19th- and early 20th-century tradition of book illustrations and broadsides. Large woodcarvings depict folk heroes and local characters of the Thousand Islands and Upper St. Lawrence River. The shop shows works in progress—engravings or letter press blocks being cut and printed—and the gallery features rustic wood furniture. Visitors can relax at the tea garden and small restaurant out back; rumor has it that the homemade peach pie is delicious!

Open Monday–Friday
9 am–4:30 pm,
Saturday
9 am–12 noon.

315-686-5722
226 James St.,
Clayton, NY
www.wingedbull.com

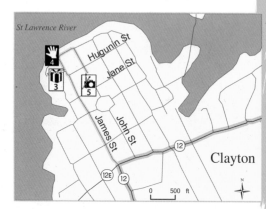

 studio
workshop

 craft
marketplace

 special
attraction

Handweaving Museum & Arts Center

In this historic Victorian, visitors will find a weaver's museum and research library. Changing multimedia exhibits and handcrafted items by area artists showcase river and mountain themes. One of the most extensive fiber libraries on the East coast.

Open daily July–August 9 am–4:30 pm. September–October closed Sunday. Winter: Monday–Friday 9 am–4:30 pm.

315-686-4123 • 314 John St., Clayton, NY

EXCURSION OFF MAIN LOOP: TAKE 1000 ISLANDS BRIDGE ($2 TOLL) OVER THE ST. LAWRENCE RIVER TO WELLESLEY ISLAND

Northern Paradise Gift Shop

Find plenty of flora, fauna, and fairies at this shop. Gifts for the body, mind, and spirit can be found from the handcrafted jewelry, quilts, decorative art, stained glass, candles, herbs, books, and rubber stamps reflecting the beauty of the region.

Open July–August: Wednesday–Sunday 12 noon–6 pm. June, September to Columbus Day: Saturday & Sunday 12 noon–6 pm.

315-482-4018 • Route 100, Wellesley Island, NY

The purple shop on the right is just past the State Park Golf Course.

Architectural Oasis

After visiting the craft shops and galleries of Wellesley Island, take a side trip to the small community of Thousand Island Park and immerse yourself in the unique collection of colorfully decorated late 19th- and early 20th-century homes concentrated in this historic district. Find classic examples of 19th-century architectural styles including Queen Anne, Eastlake, Stick style, Shingle style and Bungalow, as you stroll the quiet streets. For those yearning to learn more about the cottages found in the park, the Thousand Park Landmark Society offers precise architectural histories and descriptions.

🏠 lodging   🍴 restaurant   artist gallery

Cornwall Brothers Store and Heritage Arts Museum

Visitors will enjoy the river views and be enchanted by this museum in a historically and architecturally unique stone structure from 1866 on the banks of the St. Lawrence River. Exhibits include early mercantile articles, decorative items from the Redwood Glass Factory from the 1800s, decoys by local turn-of-the-century and present-day carvers, a locally-built St. Lawrence skiff, vintage clothing, antique motors and tools, vintage photographs, and books. The works of local artists and craftsmen are showcased in exhibits and for sale.

Open Memorial Day–late September:
Monday–Saturday 10 am–6 pm.

315-482-4033 · 36 Market St., Alexandria Bay, NY
www.alexhistorical.org

EXCURSION OFF MAIN LOOP

Sixberry Lake Campground

With 35 campsites and one 2-bedroom cabin furnished with rustic furniture, this campground with spring-fed small lake, sandy beach and wooded shoreline provides an idyllic place to spend the night or enjoy a swim. On the way in, note the Creations in Wood woodshop, which houses three separate working areas: furniture making by Mark Sears; upholstery by Mark's father, Don; and stripping by Mark's partner, Jeff.

315-628-5868 · 41797 Co. Route 21, Redwood, NY
www.rusticcreationsinwood.com

Take Rts. 26 and 190 to Rt. 37 in Redwood. Follow signs for Camp Wabasso. Turn left onto County Route 21. Go 1.5 miles to campground.

 studio workshop

 craft marketplace

 special attraction

Islander screen doors

YesterYear's Vintage Doors

9

Elegant entrances are in store here. Created in 1990 with a vision and passion for fine woodworking, the craftsmanship still harkens to the motto, "made the old fashioned way by hand." Choose from over 65 custom door styles, including traditional and period interior and exterior solid wood door designs made with only the finest premium woods.

Open year-round.

315-324-5250 · 66 S. Main St. (Route 37), Hammond, NY
www.vintagedoors.com

That Stamp Store

10

Handwoven rugs of many colors and sizes, using new cotton fabric, offer a contemporary twist to the rag rug tradition. On display at this store are placemats, runners, and mug rugs as well as a large collection of artist rubber stamps and handmade papers for cardmakers and scrapbookers.

Open Friday & Saturday 10 am–4 pm or call for hours.

315-287-3530
3975 State Hwy. 58,
Gouverneur, NY

46   lodging   restaurant   artist gallery

Wicks Pure Maple Products

Stop by to watch this third generation family make syrup and sample all things maple—cream, sugar cakes, jelly, nut fudge, barbecue sauce, and covered nuts!

Open daily 8 am–4 pm.

315-543-2737 • 7780 Route 3 West, Harrisville, NY

Croghan Meat Market, Inc.

Go back to the 19th century to the beginnings of the Croghan meat market. The interior of the meat market has been

improved over the years, but the atmosphere of the small village butcher shop remains. Old photos and tools trace the history of this long-lived business.

Open Monday–Friday 8 am–5 pm, Saturday 8 am–12 noon.

Jessie & Elmer Campany, circa 1927

315-346-6613 • 9824 N. Main St., State Route 812, Croghan, NY
www.croghanbologna.com

EXCURSION OFF MAIN LOOP: 1 MILE

Gallery 812

The places and history of Lewis County is reflected in the work of the artists found in this charming gallery. Stained glass, baskets, sterling silver jewelry, fine art prints and originals, ironwork, handweaving, knitting, crocheting, tapestry pillows, walking sticks, unique ornaments, twig furniture, handmade real fur teddy bears, pottery, bird houses, and feeders are only a beginning! New items come in weekly.

Open Wednesday–Friday 9 am–5 pm, Saturday 9 am–2 pm. Extended hours October–December.

315-376-2113 • 7899 Ridge Road, Lowville, NY
bclyndaker@westel.com

Cross bridge over the Black River on Rt. 812, turn right onto Ridge Road, go 1 mile.

 studio workshop    craft marketplace   special attraction

47

From Necessity to Art

Like many of the traditional art forms practiced in the Northern Forest, handweaving has followed a progression from practical roots to a contemporary activity valued for aesthetic appeal. Once a common skill, the advent of powered looms in the 18th century began a long decline in handweaving that continued until the early 1900s, when a handful of women revived the craft for artistic and educational purposes.

Among the leaders of this revival were Emily Kent Post, who founded the Handweaving Museum in Clayton, New York, and Berta Frey who was the first contributor to the museum library that now bears her name. Today, the Berta Frey Library is home to one of the nation's most complete collections of handweaving resources, including historic texts dating back to 1695. See the listing on page 44 for contact and location information.

EXCURSION TO FULTON: 1 MILE

Southern Cross Trading Co.

14

For more than 20 years, this business has been making indoor and outdoor furniture in contemporary and traditional styles using local cherrywood.

Open weekdays 8 am–4:30 pm.
Shop is handicapped accessible;
showroom is not handicapped accessible.

315-376-2009 • 7448 State Route 12, Lowville, NY
www.adirondackcraft.com

Located 1 mile north of Lowville on Route 12.

 lodging   restaurant   artist gallery

Pure Mist Soaps

With the stunning Black River Valley as a backdrop, Colleen Farney makes cold processed soap using original recipes.

Watch soaps being made and insulated in a mold for 2 days, then cut and placed on racks to cure for 4 to 6 weeks before packaging.

Open March–December:
Thursday & Friday
11 am–6 pm.

315-376-7676
8321 State Route 26,
Lowville, NY
www.puremistsoaps.com

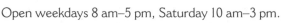

EXCURSION OFF MAIN LOOP:
1.5 MILES TO SHOWRROM

Black River Valley Woodworking

Hardwood furniture that will last a lifetime is the specialty! All furniture is custom built using selected hardwoods from the Northern states.

Open weekdays 8 am–5 pm, Saturday 10 am–3 pm.

315-376-8405 • 4773 State Route 410 • Castorland, NY

 studio workshop

 craft marketplace

 special attraction

49

Whetstone Gulf

Whether you seek an adventurous hike along its sheer 350-foot cliffs or a relaxing afternoon on a creekside beach, Whetstone Gulf State Park offers wonderful opportunities to enjoy spectacular scenic vistas. Built in and around a three-mile-long gorge in the eastern edge of the Tug Hill Plateau, the park features campsites and picnic areas alongside the creek at the base of the gorge, as well as hiking trails for a variety of skill levels. Those interested in exploring the loop trail along the top of the gorge should note that it is restricted to people age 18 and older, and no one is allowed to embark after 3 pm. Open from Memorial Day to Labor Day, and from December 15 through March 15 for winter recreation, the park is located off Route 26, six miles south of Lowville.

 lodging   restaurant artist gallery

Chapter
4

Gateways to the Adirondacks

Whether you come from the west or the east, the artisans and craftspeople of the Adirondack Gateway Tours will welcome you to their communities as well as the studios, workshops, and galleries where they create and exhibit fine handmade products. Two distinct tours serve as your southern gateways to the arts and crafts of the Adirondack region.

Entering from the west and the Rome/Utica region, the Central Adirondack Tour winds through some of the deepest wilderness you can experience from the comfort of a car. This tour starts in Rome with a very scenic drive north to Boonville and a short excursion to Port Leyden. Then join the main loop to head east and north toward Old Forge, where the offerings range from the fine arts of the Old Forge Art Center to crafts including fiber, wood, pottery, tin, and glass.

Photo by:
Carl Heilman II

Stop by the Great Camp Sagamore to learn about the magnificent rustic "camps" that flourished in the Adirondacks during the early 20th century. Continue your history lesson at the Adirondack Museum before immersing yourself in the galleries of the Adirondack Lakes Center for the Arts in Blue Mountain Lake. Discover hidden treasures as you circle back south through the heart of the Adirondack wilderness and the tiny communities tucked away in the dense forest.

A more cosmopolitan though still rustic experience awaits those entering the region from the east to explore the Lower Adirondack Tour. Anchored by Saratoga Springs with its bustling downtown and historic racetrack, this tour can be followed as a single long loop or broken up into three smaller loops—each of which makes a wonderful day trip.

From Saratoga Springs, head east toward Salem and northwest toward Glens Falls, stopping at the wonderful array of craft galleries and pottery studios along the way. En route, take an excursion out to the buffalo farm and workshop in Fort Ann where Yvonne Phillips continues a generations-old Abenaki basket-weaving tradition. Follow Route 4 to Glens Falls and explore the gallery and gift shop of the Lower Adirondack Regional Arts Council.

An extensive excursion to some of the smaller communities north of Lake George makes a fine day trip in itself. You'll find fine art and crafts ranging from pottery to antler lighting, hand-built custom furniture and home décor. (Traveler's tip: "Rt. 9N" does not signify north, so double-check your direction when following 9N.)

Returning to the main route south of Lake George, head west, stopping to peruse the many galleries before crossing the spectacular Hudson River and Great Lake Sacandaga. Finish your trip with a visit to the Adirondack Handweavers in Gloversville, then return to Saratoga Springs.

Let the Central and Lower Adirondack Tours be your gateways not just to the Adirondack Park, but to the culture and traditions of the people who call this place home.

Cultural Heritage Profile

Forever Wild

"The lands of the state, now owned or hereafter acquired, constituting the forest preserve as now fixed by law, shall be forever kept as wild forest lands. They shall not be leased, sold or exchanged, or be taken by any corporation, public or private, nor shall the timber thereon be sold, removed or destroyed."

Nothing defines the Adirondacks more powerfully than this clause, which was added to the New York State Constitution in 1895.

Encompassing roughly 6 million acres, the Adirondack Park is larger than Yellowstone, Yosemite, Glacier, and Grand Canyon national parks combined. It includes 3,000 lakes, 30,000 miles of rivers and streams, 46 mountain peaks over 4,000 feet, and important natural habitats including unique wetlands and old growth forests.

Support for protection of the Adirondacks first grew in the mid-1800s in response to two primary factors. First was the rapid depletion of the region's forests by loggers supplying wood to growing lumber, paper, and tannery operations. Second was the sheer splendor of the region's wild and rugged landscape—which was drawing more and more people in search of temporary escape from the congested cities of the eastern United States.

In response to prodding from a wide range of advocates, the New York State Legislature first acted to establish a forest preserve in the Adirondacks in 1885, and by 1895 the region was awarded the constitutional protection it now enjoys.

Today, the 2.7 million acres of state-owned forest preserve included within the park represent the largest wild forest area in the eastern United States. The remaining private lands include cities, villages and hamlets, timberlands, farms, businesses, homes and camps—all subject to land use regulation by the Adirondack Park Agency. This unique mix of public and private lands has established the Adirondack Park as a model for conservation in other parts of the country and the world.

Whether it's a guide boat designed for exploring the wild waterways or a luminous landscape painting, you'll find the influence of the Adirondack's "forever wild" forests infusing the region's traditions work of its artists and craftspeople. While you're exploring the handcraft traditions of Lewis, Jefferson and St. Lawrence counties, don't forget to enjoy the fresh produce and savory handcrafted foods and preserves from the local farms.

Photo by: Carl Heilman II

Central Adirondacks

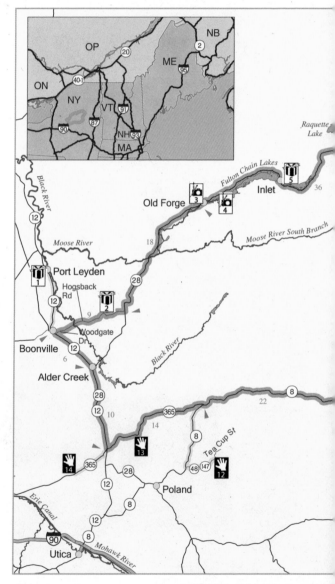

The main portion of the Central Adirondac

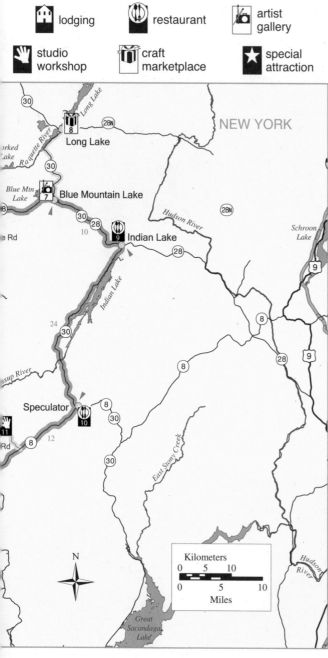

| | lodging | | restaurant | | artist gallery |
| | studio workshop | | craft marketplace | | special attraction |

NEW YORK

(30)
Long Lake
Long Lake
(28N)

orked Lake
Roquette River
(30)

Blue Mtn Lake
Blue Mountain Lake
7

Hudson River
(28N)

(30) (28)
10
Indian Lake
9

Schroon Lake

e Rd
(28)

Indian Lake

(9)

24
(30)

8

ssup River

8
(28)
(9)

Speculator
8
10
(30)

11
Rd
8
12

30

East Stony Creek

N

| Kilometers |
| 0 5 10 |
| 0 5 10 |
| Miles |

Hudson River

Great Sacandaga Lake

oop is approximately 161 miles long.

CENTRAL ADIRONDACKS

This route begins with an excursion to Port Leyden from Boonville. From Rome take Rt. 46 (the Gorge Road) to Boonville.

EXCURSION TO PORT LEYDEN

A Quilted Heart

Inside an 1885 church with eye-catching stained glass and stenciling, this shop offers the highest quality of quilting fabrics, books, patterns, and notions. Find quilts of all types— from the most traditional blocks to contemporary patterns. Lessons for beginner and experienced quilters are scheduled monthly.

Quilted wall hanging made from a Pine Needles, Inc. pattern

Open Monday–Friday 10 am–5 pm, Saturday 10 am–4 pm. Partially handicapped accessible.

315-348-4544 • 3331 Lincoln St., Port Leyden, NY
www.aquiltedheart.com

From NY State Rt. 12, at light in Port Leyden, turn east, go one block, turn left onto Lincoln. Big tan church on left.

Creekside Gifts & Antiques

Come into the woods and visit some of yesterday's rustic country charm. A shop filled with antique furniture and the largest Christmas corner around! Find a treasure of the woods to accent a home, camp, or cottage. Adirondack-style furniture and accessories are hand-crafted by proprietor Dale Ferris using white birch, cherry, pine, and even deer antlers! Don't forget a little something for your taste buds,

Snowshoe lamp & shelf

 lodging   restaurant   artist gallery

too. Maple syrup, jams and jellies, salsas, and tomato sauce are all local.

315-392-4639 • 7015 Round Lake Road, Boonville, NY

*From Boonville take the Hawkinsville/Hogsback Road to Woodgate;
7 miles from Boonville/Rt. 12, turn right onto Round Lake Road
(0.2 miles on right).*

Artworks, Inc

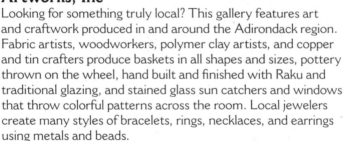

Looking for something truly local? This gallery features art and craftwork produced in and around the Adirondack region. Fabric artists, woodworkers, polymer clay artists, and copper and tin crafters produce baskets in all shapes and sizes, pottery thrown on the wheel, hand built and finished with Raku and traditional glazing, and stained glass sun catchers and windows that throw colorful patterns across the room. Local jewelers create many styles of bracelets, rings, necklaces, and earrings using metals and beads.

315-369-2007 • 3062 Main St., Old Forge, NY
ggoven@capital.net

Continue east on Hawkinsville/Hogsback Road to Rt. 28.

Great Camps, Great Times

Pioneered by William West Durant's Camp Pine Knot around 1880, the Adirondack Great Camp occupies a distinctive and important place in the history of American architecture. Characterized by log construction, native stonework, decorative twig and branch designs, and multi-building complexes, these luxurious though classically rustic retreats proliferated in the late 19th and early 20th centuries as wealthy industrialists and financiers sought retreat and relaxation in the wilderness.

Today, the rustic buildings common to the national and state park systems across the United States often exhibit the influence of the Adirondack Great Camps in their use of local materials and low-impact site integration. Though the forest has reclaimed many of the original Adirondack camps, public tours and educational programs are available at the Great Camp Sagamore. See the listing on page 61 for more information.

studio workshop — craft marketplace — special attraction

Northern Forest Canoe Trail

From Old Forge, New York, to Fort Kent, Maine, the Northern Forest Canoe Trail runs 740 miles across the headwaters of every major river system in the Northeast. Once central to the lives of Native Americans and European settlers, today this network of travel routes offers unsurpassed opportunities for canoe and kayak recreation as well as endless lessons about the heritage of the Northern Forest.

While it includes many wild and remote areas, the NFCT also passes through villages, small cities, and areas that have witnessed both the development and abandonment of industry. Paddling its entire length takes about eight weeks and requires all the skills a canoeist can muster—flat-water, whitewater, portaging, poling, and paddling upriver and down. For those less experienced or lacking time for a complete passage, many sections of the trail are suitable for shorter, less demanding trips.

For more information, visit the information kiosk at the start of the trail in Old Forge, or visit www.northernforestcanoetrail.org.

Arts Center of Old Forge

Performing and visual arts come together. The main exhibits feature Adirondack themes and showcase fine arts and watercolor paintings, quilts, and individual gallery exhibits. Check the calendar for performances, workshops, and special events!

Open Monday–Saturday 10 am–4 pm,
Sunday 12 noon–4 pm. Closed Sundays in Winter.
Fees for performances and competitive exhibits.

315-369-6411 · Route 28, Old Forge, NY
www.artscenteroldforge.org

The Arts Center is north of the village on Route 28.

lodging   restaurant   artist gallery

Black Bear Trading Post

An amazing Adirondack quilt shop. Three thousand bolts of Adirondack fabric, cherrywood, cottons, flannels, batiks, fleece, upholstery, and decorator fabric can be found.

Open daily 10 am. Call for closing hour. January–March: Friday–Monday 10 am, call for closing hour.

315-357-5092
115 Route 28, Inlet, NY

Located just before Inlet, opposite Stiefvater's Lakeside Cottages

EXCURSION OFF THE MAIN LOOP

Great Camp Sagamore

Gilded age splendor in the woods. Don't miss this National Historic Landmark, a 27-building vintage Vanderbilt Estate. Guided tours will expose the full flavor of traditions and lingering landmarks of this era.

Open daily mid-May–mid-October 9:30 am–4:30 pm.

315-354-5311 • Sagamore Road, Raquette Lake, NY
www.sagamore.org

Turn right onto Sagamore Rd. off Rt. 28; go 4 miles. Retrace steps to main loop.

 studio workshop

 craft marketplace

 special attraction

Adirondack Lakes Center for the Arts
7

A three-gallery complex features artists from the Northern Forest and around the country. All media from painting to pottery, photography, and quilting are included in the exhibit calendar.

Open year-round. $12 for most concerts, admission for workshops.

**518-352-7715 · Main Street, Route 28, Blue Mountain Lake, NY
www.adk-arts.org**

The Arts Center is on the right as you arrive in town, a tan building next to the Post Office.

EXCURSION TO LONG LAKE

Hoss's Country Corner
8

Don't miss this original country store dating back to 1878! Find treasures and gifts among the Native American crafts, paintings, antiques, furniture, quilts, jewelry, and maple syrup or peruse the large Adirondack book collection. Small shops are in cabins in back.

Summer: 9 am–10 pm. Winter: 9:30 am–5:30 pm.

800-952-HOSS · Lake Street, Long Lake, NY

Lake Street is at the junction of Route 30 and 28N.

RETURN TO BLUE MOUNTAIN LAKE AND HEAD SOUTHWEST TOWARD INDIAN LAKE

Marty's Chili Nights
9

Authentic Mexican Cuisine in a wide variety of freshly made dishes including many vegetarian choices and children's menu. Relax in the colorful dining rooms combining Adirondack charm with Mexican décor, listen to traditional bandas and other lively Hispanic music. Reservations are always taken, and strongly recommended during July, August and all holidays.

Open year round, hours change seasonally.

518-648-5832 · Rt. 28, Indian Lake, NY · www.chilinights.com

 lodging · restaurant

 artist gallery

A History of HandMade Creativity

From snowshoes to soaps, baskets to boats, many of the handmade products in this guidebook are rooted in functional traditions and a time when making things by hand was the only option. Early inhabitants of the Adirondacks, and the broader Northern Forest region, had to be creative as they carved lives for themselves from the forest landscape.

Few places offer more compelling opportunities to learn about the traditions of handmade products that once defined life, work, travel and play in the region than the Adirondack Museum. From its extensive collections of rustic Adirondack furniture and structures to hand-painted signs, wood carvings, baskets, traditional fiber arts, hand-blown glass, tools, and the second largest watercraft collection in the country, the museum's exhibits and historic structures offer endless insights into the history and creativity that underlie many of the handmade products featured in this guide. Stop by on your way through Blue Mountain Lake (midway between Lake George and Lake Placid on Rt. 30). Open Memorial Day–Oct. www.adkmuseum.org

Common Grounds Café

Locally owned and operated by the McIntyre sisters since 1999, this eatery is a favorite of both locals and visitors. Tastefully and comfortably furnished, it is situated in the center of town among the breathtaking Adirondack Mountains. Homemade soups, fresh baked goods and specialty coffees fill the cafe with mouthwatering aroma. A small gallery of art features handcrafted items by local artisans

Open Monday, Wednesday–Saturday 7 am–2 pm,
Sunday 8 am–12 noon.

518-548-5488 · Four Corners on Rt. 30/8, Speculator, NY
www.villagerentalsny.com/commongroundscafe.htm

The tiny town of Piseco supports K-8 education for its 16 students through an innovative partnership that combines the local school with the public library, a fitness center, and the Cornell University Cooperative Extension.

 studio
workshop

 craft
marketplace

 special
attraction

Truly Adirondack Crafts

Find Adirondack-style rustic furnishings made using native materials—from twig pencils to king-size beds! Custom items to accent the home include tables, lamps, frames, benches, stools, with a specialization in white birch frames, mirrors, and stands.

Open mid-April–November. Custom orders year-round. Call for appointment.

518-548-8717 · Piseco, NY
tacbw@telenet.net

From Rt. 8, take Old Piseco Road. Look for Golden Sands sign; turn left and go 300 feet.

EXCURSION OFF THE MAIN LOOP TO COLD BROOK

Woodland Essence

Tucked in the evergreen forest of the southern Adirondacks, Kate Gilday has built a family-run business honoring the beauty and healing nature of plants and the land. Woodland gardens harbor medicinal plants including Goldenseal, American Ginseng and Blue Cohash. The teaching center is busy in June, when baskets are crafted using the whole bark of white ash trees gathered in an ecologically-sensitive manner and laced with the inner bark of hickory.

315-845-1515 · 392 Tea Cup St., Cold Brook, NY
woodland@ntcnet.com

From Cold Brook hamlet on Rt. 8, go 5 miles on Gray Road. Return north on Rt. 8 to rejoin main loop.

 lodging   restaurant   artist gallery

Tidbits

Forest Hollow

Two intertwined studios of long-time artists can be found here. Bruce, a photographer for journals such as *Audubon Magazine*, and an earthenware potter, may be on the wheel when visitors stop by. Cathy, a metalsmith and painter, labors over sterling silver jewelry, using the same bold colors and strong lines of her "Pop Art meets Surrealism" paintings. Whimsically painted furniture is also on display.

315-826-7162 • 998 Route 365, Hinckley, NY

Turn south onto Rt. 365 from Rt. 8.

Art Baird Pottery

Behind an 1870s stick style home, Art Baird finds inspiration in

his pottery studio and gallery. Located in a 100-year-old barn—formerly a livery stable —Art performs heel thrown, wheel thrown, and hand built functional pottery. Find works for the home and garden, such as bird feeders and planters.

Open Saturday & Sunday 10 am–3 pm.

888-353-9620 • 9527 Cotes Road, Holland Patent, NY
www.artbairdpottery.com

Follow Rt. 365 south across Rt. 12; continue to center of village of Holland Patent. Access to studio is through garden gate.

To return to Rome, continue south on Rt. 365. To reach Utica, go north on Rt. 365 to intersection with Rt. 12, then south to Rt. 8.

 studio workshop

 craft marketplace

 special attraction

Lower Adirondacks

The main portion of the Lower Adirondac[k]

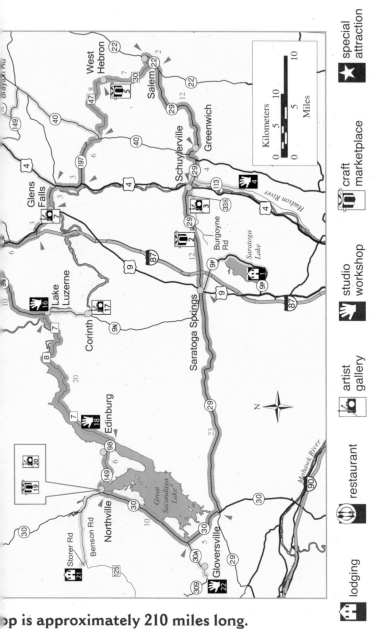

op is approximately 210 miles long.

LOWER ADIRONDACKS

Saratoga Lake Inn and Bistro, Inc.

Overlooking Saratoga Lake, this Inn provides more than just comfortable rooms. Guests can enjoy a day at the beach, a wander into downtown Saratoga Springs or a sunset dinner at the Bistro on the deck above the lake.

Open May–September. Winter reduced hours.
Lunch and dinner daily, 11:00 am–10:00 pm.

518-587-8280 • 511 Rt. 9P, Saratoga Lake, NY
www.saratogalakebistro.com

Schuyler Pond Home & Garden

The floor and loft of this restored 1850s dairy barn showcases an eclectic array of fine gifts and home furnishings from local artisans.

Open Summer: Tuesday–Saturday 10 am–5 pm, Sunday 12 noon–5 pm. Winter: Wednesday–Saturday 10 am–5 pm, Sunday 12 noon–5 pm.

518-581-8422 • 727 Route 29, Saratoga Springs, NY

5 miles east of Saratoga Springs.

Saratoga Clayworks

Two types of work can be found at this studio. Doug Klein makes functional and decorative stoneware and porcelain. His wheel thrown and slab built vessels and tiles are embellished with relief imagery. Darren Prodger creates wheel thrown functional and decorative stoneware and porcelain pots.

Open Wednesday–Friday 11 am–5 pm.

518-695-3602 • 100 Burgoyne Road, Schuylerville, NY
saratogaclayworks@earthlink.net

Turn right on Rt. 338 for 1 mile.

 lodging   restaurant   artist gallery

Masters & Modernists

Take a break from your tour of handmade and traditional crafts to enjoy the works of the some of world's finest classical artists.

The Hyde Collection is a historic house and art museum complex that combines Adirondack heritage with a world-class collection of works by European masters and American artists, important decorative arts, and antique furnishings. Over 50 years, the museum's founders, Louis and Charlotte Hyde, assembled 2,800 works spanning the history of Western art from the 4th century B.C.E. to the 20th century. The collection features works by Old Masters such as Botticelli, Raphael, and Rembrandt; modern masters including Cézanne, Degas, Picasso, Renoir, and van Gogh; and important American artists including Eakins, Hassam, and Homer.

Located at 161 Warren Street, Glens Falls, the Hyde Collection is open year-round Tuesday–Saturday 10 am–5 pm, and Sunday noon–5 pm. Admission is free. For information, call 518-792-1761 or visit www.hydecollection.org.

Blue Moon Clay Studio

This studio showcases and sells two complimentary styles of work. With an affinity for classic forms and unglazed work, Brenda McMahon makes sagger-fired porcelain vessels and tiles. John Visser creates diverse functional and sculptural forms—from large vessels to unique coffee cups.

Classes allow the creative and curious to try a hand at the potter's wheel, sculpt a garden goddess or gargoyle, or learn ancient hand building methods.

Open May–December: weekends 11 am–5 pm, or by chance.

518-692-7742 · 2242 Route 113, Greenwich, NY
www.bluemoonclay.com

To reach the studio, continue on Rt. 338 past the Saratoga Monument and in Schuylverville take Rt. 4/32 (0.25 mile) to Rt. 29. Cross Champlain Canal/Hudson River and turn right on Rt. 113 for 5 miles.

 studio workshop

 craft marketplace

 special attraction

69

Gardenworks

5

Find a range of agricultural delights in this converted dairy barn. Thousands of farm grown flowers can be found in the drying area and a retail space showcases original floral arrangements and wreaths. Local craftspeople sell homemade soap, metal art, candles, and custom birdhouses. Food bounty includes U-pick blueberries, raspberries, fall pumpkins, gourds, homegrown Christmas trees, and hand-tied wreaths. Columbus Day weekend brings a celebration of the harvest season with food tastings, demonstrations, and workshops.

Open April–December: Tuesday–Saturday 9 am–5 pm, Sunday 1·am–5 pm.

518-854-3250 · 464 Scott Lake Road, 1055 Route 30, Salem, NY · www.gardenworksfarm.com

From the village of Salem turn onto County Route 30. Travel 5 miles and Gardenworks Barn is on left.

Racing Through Time

In much of the Northern Forest, horses have long been valued for their strength and sure-footedness in hauling loads of logs out of the woods. Here in Saratoga Springs, though, they are valued for something quite different—pure speed.

For more than 140 years, fans have flocked to the Saratoga Race Course to watch the most elite horses in the world compete in one of the world's most beautiful and historic racing venues. The Saratoga course is, in fact, the oldest operating thoroughbred racetrack in the nation, and each year, from late July through the first week in September, it comes to life with regular races, music, and celebration of one of America's oldest sporting traditions.

Whether you cheer a winner or enjoy a quiet morning breakfast watching the horses work out, the racetrack at Saratoga offers a truly unique experience.

 lodging   restaurant   artist gallery

Honest Injun' Baskets and Winchell Creek Beefalo Farm

Cross Winchell Creek to arrive at this 200-year-old farmstead with red barn, basket shop, pasture-fed beefaloos, and free-ranging hens. Collectors of Native American baskets appreciate Yvonne's fourth generation Abernaki fancy baskets. Visitors can find Easter baskets, flower holders, Adirondack pack baskets, candle baskets, arrow quivers, fishing (tip up) baskets, wine baskets, gift baskets, and letter holders.

Open Saturday & Sunday 10 am–4 pm.

518-642-9600 • 676 East Starbuck Lane, Fort Ann, NY • gunnar@netheaven.com

Take Rt. 40 to Rt. 149. Turn right on Rt. 17 for 5 miles, then right on to Brayton Rd. for 1 mile and left onto East Starbuck Lane.

Yvonne Phillips with some of her baskets

Return to main loop by retracing your steps to Rt. 149, then following it west to Rt. 4. Follow Rt. 4 south into Glens Falls and turn right onto Warren Street.

Lower Adirondack Regional Arts Council/ LARAC

Founded in 1972, the Arts Council welcomes visitors to this large gallery and gift shop. Monthly exhibits feature artists and artisans from the region.

Open weekdays 10 am–3 pm, Saturday 9 am–3 pm.

518-798-1144 • 7 Lapham Pl., Glens Falls, NY • www.larac.org

Take Rte 9L/Ridge Road/St. to parking lot next to City Hall at 42 Ridge St.

The next 9 listings create a lengthy excursion off of the main loop from Lake George to Schroon Lake and warrant a day trip of their own.

Tidbits

Dr. Thomas Durant, who built the first railroad into the Adirondacks between 1865 and 1871, was one of two men who drove the golden spike at Promintory Point, Utah that linked the nation's first transcontinental railroad.

 studio workshop

 craft marketplace

 special attraction

71

Thomas W. Brady Furnituremaker

8

Thomas Brady makes original furniture inspired by Shaker and Mission designs. All pieces are handmade from native hardwoods— including figured maples, cherry, walnut, oak, and birch—and given a handrubbed finish.

Open daily, call for hours.

518-644-9801 · 4635 Lakeshore Dr., Bolton Landing, NY
www.adirondackwood.com/ businesses/bradysfurniture/index.html

After leaving LARAC, take Rt. 87 (winner of Scenic Highway Award) north to exit 24. Go east on Rt. 11 to Rt. 9. Go to Bolton Landing. The shop is 1 mile south of Bolton Landing on Lakeshore Drive.

Country Road Lodge B&B

9

Relax at this secluded bed & breakfast that has been operating on the Hudson River since 1974. Roam the forty acres of field and woodland, surrounded by Adirondack state forests or retire in one of the four comfortable guest rooms and enjoy a country-style breakfast.

Open daily.

518-623-2207
115 Hickory Hill Road,
Warrensburg, NY
www.countryroadlodge.com

Look for sign for Diamond Point Rd. 6 miles south of Bolton Landing at church. Follow Diamond Point Rd. into Warrensburg.

Theodore Roosevelt was hiking on Mount Marcy when he was summoned to be sworn in as president of the United States after the assassination of President McKinley at the World's Fair in Buffalo.

Tidbits

 lodging restaurant artist gallery

Comfort & Style

Few pleasures match the feeling of sitting back on a camp porch watching the sun set over a calm lake while an icy drink forms a ring on the wide, flat arm of your Adirondack chair. Designed in 1903 by Thomas Lee of Westport, New York, and patented by Harry Brunnell in 1904, these chairs were first known as Westport Plank chairs. Thought they are ubiquitous and mass produced in many places, you can still find authentic, handcrafted versions of these classic chairs in the Adirondacks.

If your taste runs more toward the rustic furniture style—with its stick and twig construction, birch bark decoration, and elaborate design, you'll find that its roots run deep in the Adirondacks as well.

Whatever your preference, be sure to visit the many fine furniture makers featured in this guide to capture an authentic piece of Adirondack history and heritage.

Fawn Ridge Pottery

Each piece of pottery by clay artist David J. Coleman is glazed with dishwasher-safe, lead-free glazes. The showroom is fully stocked with colorful and functional stoneware pottery and clay artworks—mugs, bowls, dinnerware, casseroles, dip dishes, platters, goblets, and pitchers. Artworks range from realistic scenes of the Adirondacks painted on platters and plates to serious and whimsical sculptures.

Open Summer: 10 am–5 pm. Closed Wednesday.
Fall: 10 am–5 pm. Closed Tuesday & Wednesday.
Winter: by chance or appointment.

518-494-4373 · 34 Fawn Ridge Road, Chestertown, NY
www.fawn-ridge-pottery.com

Follow signs from Rt. 28 to Potter Brook Road (2 miles)
to Fawn Ridge Road (1 mile).

 studio workshop

 craft marketplace

 special attraction

The Rustic Homestead Streamside Gallery

Visitors will be charmed with this 1200-square-foot gallery showroom with cathedral ceilings and a stream running out back. The gallery specializes in high-end rustic furniture and antler lighting. Find dining sets, rockers, entertainment centers, and decorative antiques.

Open Monday–Saturday 10 am–4 pm.

518-251-4038 • Corner 28N and Main St., North Creek, NY
www.rustichomestead.com

Back to Rt. 28 west to Rt. 28N. Turn right on 28N, go one block. First building on the right past the intersection.

The Lemon Potpourri

Take a break for tea or a stroll over the footbridge into the garden at the Four Corners in Olmstedville. There are upside-down pots, unusual and old-fashioned kitchenware, tea and accessories, rustic items, handmade woolens, and homemade jams and jellies all made by local artists and artisans. You can also find unique garden statuary and other garden items.

Open May: Friday, Saturday & Sunday 10 am–6 pm.
June–August: Thursday–Monday 10 am–6 pm.
September–Columbus Day: Friday–Sunday 10 am–5 pm.
Columbus Day–December: Saturday & Sunday 10 am–5 pm.
Please call ahead for additions to these hours.

Call ahead to check for additional hours.

518-251-2093 • Four Corners, Route 29/30, Olmstedville, NY

Continue east on Rt. 28N.

Adirondack LogWorks and the Scalloped Edge Bed & Breakfast

Visitors are in awe of this hand-hewn log and stone house and B&B made from materials on the property. Scott Phillips builds log furniture, railings, stairs, and home décor in his basement studio by hand-peeling wood with a drawknife.

Open June–August: Tuesday & Wednesday 1 am–5 pm.

518-532-9473 • 22 Covell Road, Schroon Lake, NY
www.adirondacklogworks.com

From Olmstedville take Trout Brook Road. Turn right on Hoffman Road, immediate left on Covell Road. Look for first house, log and stone house on right with red metal roof.

 lodging   restaurant   artist gallery

Scenic Outlook Studios

Lisa Steres specializes in hand-thrown original works of art with a practical dimension. She developed her craft and love for making beautiful, functional pottery with some of the most talented production potters in Virginia, Massachusetts and upstate New York. Her studies have taken her to Japan, where she explored pottery styles and lantern designs all over the country.

Open Memorial Day–Labor Day: 10 am–6 pm,
Labor Day–Columbus Day: closed Mon & Tues,
Columbus Day–Christmas: Friday–Sunday.
January–May: by appointment.

518-494-5367 • 440 Riverside Station Road, Riparius, NY
www.scenicoutlookstudios.com

Continue south on Rt. 9 from Schroon Lake, then take Rt. 8 east for 5 miles. Cross the red bridge over the Hudson River. Turn left directly after the bridge. Scenic Outlook Studios is the second building on the left next to the train station.

Red Truck Pottery

Bill Knoble has been making stoneware functional pottery, specializing in kitchenware, ovenware, and dinnerware since 1973. His work is handthrown, gas- and wood-fired, and

glazed in strong solid colors or hand decorated. "We use local minerals and clays for glazes, and anorthosite as a ceramic material. Anorthosite is the primary rock constituting the geology of the High Peaks region of the Adirondacks. To the best of our knowledge, we are the only pottery on the planet using this material in production."

Open May–October: Thursday–Tuesday 10 am–5 pm.

518-494-2074 • 11 Dennehy Road, Chestertown, NY
bill@netheaven.com

Return to Rt.9 and head south. Dennehy Road will be on left.

 studio workshop

 craft marketplace

 special attraction

Lynn Benevento Gallery

Lynn Benevento paints local scenes and landscapes that mirror the Adirondacks in all seasons. Her realistic paintings capture the beauty of wild flowers, barns, hot air balloons, mountains, and lakes. The gallery carries her work as original paintings, framed and unframed prints, and notecards.

Open Seasonally.

518-696-5702
Four Bridge St., Lake Luzerne, NY
www.lynnbenevento.com

From Warrensburg, take I-87 south to exit 20. Head north on Rt. 9 and then west on 9N/Luzerne Road. Turn right at high school onto Mill Street. At stop sign at bottom of hill turn left onto Main Street. Take next right onto Bridge Street. Gallery is on right.

"Hepatica" painting by Lynn Benevento

EXCURSION OFF THE MAIN LOOP TO CORNISH

McArthur Park Gateway Gallery

This gallery guarantees an Adirondack experience for everyone. Adirondack-style furniture and accessories, specialty lighting, taxidermy, antler chandeliers, candles, and paintings represent local talent. Baskets are made by 4th-generation Abenaki Indians and other fine traditional crafts are available.

🏠 lodging   🍽 restaurant   artist gallery

Proceeds from the gallery support McArthur Park's mission to enrich the lives of children experiencing a life-changing impact.

Open April–December. January–March by appointment.

518-654-9828 • 126 Maple St., Corinth, NY
www.mcarthurpark.org

Travel south on Rt. 9N. Turn right onto Mill St. after light.

The Dodge House Lakeside Gallery

Constance Dodge's studio and gallery of paintings is on the second floor of this Victorian 1850s home overlooking the Great Sacandaga Lake by the Batchellerville Bridge. Her work challenges the representation of time and place through two-dimensional images. "Thematically, I am interested in

liberating images of people from old photographs, postcards, and albums to provide an idiom suggestive of an individual's destiny. These fragmented moments of everyday life suggest the evanescence of time and the mystery of existence."

Open June–October:
Wednesday–Saturday 12 noon–5 pm.

518-863-2201
936 South Shore Road,
Edinburg, NY
Cdodgeart@frontiernet.net

Adirondack Country Store

Rustic and Adirondack furniture galore! Cedar log beds and futons are among the pottery, jewelry, and birch bark handcrafts made exclusively by a local craftsmen. This is a great place to find that special gift or decorative accessory, such as a grandfather style birch clock.

Open daily.

518-863-6056
252 No. Main St., Northville, NY
www.adirondackcountrystore.com

 studio
workshop

 craft
marketplace

 special
attraction

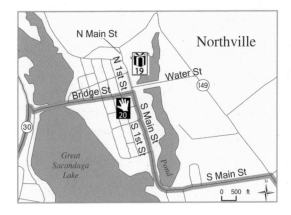

The Commonground Gallery

Anne Miller teaches guitar, piano, violin, mandolin, and banjo in her working studio in a restored 19th-century blacksmith

shop. Students and visitors can also view her oil and watercolor paintings, pastels, and drawings that explore the landscape of the southern Adirondacks and Sacandaga River Valley.

Open weekdays 10 am–5 pm, Saturday & Sunday 11 am–3 pm. Closed Monday.

518-863-4693
122 Bridge St., Northville, NY
www.annemiller.com

From Main St., take Bridge St. west. Gallery is on left in first block.

Saggar fired porcelain

EXCURSION OFF THE MAIN LOOP
WEST OF NORTHVILLE

Lapland Lake Cross-Country Ski and Vacation Center

Founded more than a quarter of a century ago by former U.S. Olympic cross country skier Olavi Hirvonen, this unique Finnish-flavored resort is situated on hundreds of carefully managed acres. Its mountain setting, combined with cozy, comfortable surroundings and the warm hospitality of the

 lodging   restaurant   artist gallery

Hirvonen family, create an idyllic setting for recreation and relaxation every season of the year.

Open daily.

518-863-4974 • 139 Lapland Lake Road, Northville, NY
www.laplandlake.com

From Northville, take Rt. 30 north. Turn left onto the Benson Rd. (County Hwy. 6) for 5.2 miles. At Storer Road, turn right and continue 0.75 miles, bearing right.

Lapland Lake Cross-Country Ski and Vacation Center

Adirondack Handweavers

A step into this 175-year-old home opens a world of handwoven textile history and design. The studio specializes in early American patterns and adaptation to modern usage. Several looms, including an antique barn frame loom (on view during summer months only), are in operation. Ms. Gene E. Valk has been weaving household linens, afghans, coverlets, rugs, scarves, and shawls for over 60 years. She is happy to

demonstrate pattern, tape, or rag rug weaving on request. Come for a class in the spring or stop in for a look through one-of-a-kind towels, napkins, place mats, table runners, mug rugs, and chair seat covers. Some clothing items are woven or knitted from handspun yarn.

Open year-round.

518-725-3371 • 402 North Main St., Gloversville, NY

Bear right off Rt. 30 onto Rt. 30A. Turn west on Rt. 349; continue into city on East State Street to blinking light at intersection with North Main Street. Turn left on N. Main Street and follow through two intersections. Studio is in middle of third block. Look for "Weefhuis Studio" sign with "Adirondack Handweavers" attached below.

 studio
workshop

 craft
marketplace

 special
attraction

Chapter 5

Lake Champlain

Considered the sixth Great Lake by many, the 108-mile-long Lake Champlain runs north and south between the Adirondack Mountains in New York and the Green Mountains of Vermont, emptying to the north into the St. Lawrence River. Admire mountain views and fine art and handcrafts in both its Vermont and New York shore communities on this two- to three-day circuit.

Begin in Shelburne, Vermont, exploring the 45-acre campus of the Shelburne Craft School and Gallery before heading north to Burlington, the region's most cosmopolitan city. While you're

Photos by: Carl Heilman II

in town, browse your way along Church Street, head up the hill to the University of Vermont campus, wander down to the lake for a sunset stroll, and sample the many fine art and craft galleries and restaurants.

From Burlington, continue on to the lake's northern islands and the crossing into New York. You can stand in the bow of the ferry and feel the breeze and, sometimes, the spray from the lake during the 20-minute ferry trip. If you prefer dry land, drive north along the causeways from island to island and cross the Rouses Point Bridge. Heading south along the New York side of the lake, you'll find artists and craftspeople who draw inspiration from the dual influences of the lake to their east and the Adirondack Mountains to their west.

Before recrossing the lake into Vermont, pause to enjoy the view of Lake Champlain from Crown Point—site of many important maritime battles during the 18th and 19th centuries, and a popular spot for catching a glimpse of the reputed local sea monster, Champ. After crossing the Crown Point Bridge, the fine craft galleries and studios in historic Middlebury will capture your attention. Save your energy, though, for the many sites and attractions you'll find as you meander back north along the western slope of the Green Mountains.

Enjoy the glorious sunset over the lake and the Adirondacks as you complete your journey.

Cultural Heritage Profile

Conserving Culture at the Vermont Folklife Center

If Thanksgiving mud holds up a duck, the rest of the winter will wallow in muck.

If Candlemas Day be fair and bright, Winter will take another flight.

When the wind's in the west, the sap flows best.

A cold wet May means a barn full of hay. A hot dry June, sings a different tune.

These bits of folklore are just a few of the many sayings that help Vermonters manage their time and activities through long brutal winters, mud season, summers that are all too short, and glorious autumn days. They also are a sampling of the wealth of folklore and folklife materials that have been collected and preserved by the Vermont Folklife Center.

The Center is nationally recognized as a leader in the emerging field of cultural conservation. Through ongoing field research, a multimedia archive and an apprenticeship program, staff members of the Center work to preserve Vermont's intangible heritage—the skills, talents, and traditions passed down informally through generations, and the every-day experiences of people today.

With offices, exhibit space and a retail shop in downtown Middlebury, the Center documents the past and present by capturing the voices and works of Vermonters. Staff members research and preserve the historic and contemporary folklife of Vermont communities through audio and video interviews, photography, traditional arts apprenticeships, exhibits, publications, workshops and educational outreach.

The Vermont Folklife Center Archive contains the products of this ethnographic research work. The archive holds a wealth of folklife materials preserved on an array of media formats—including more than 3,800 audio taped interviews, approximately 200 video tapes, 15,000 slides and photographs, manuscripts, and other documentation organized into over 100 distinct collections. The holdings are constantly growing.

Contact the VFC archivist for more information about your particular areas of interest, or stop by the Center to explore the exhibits and purchase authentic traditional folk art from the retail store.

And, if you're visiting Vermont or any part of the Northern Forest in the summer, be sure to make the best of the weather. Around here we only have two seasons—nine months of winter, and three months of darn poor sledding!

lodging restaurant artist gallery

Lake Champlain

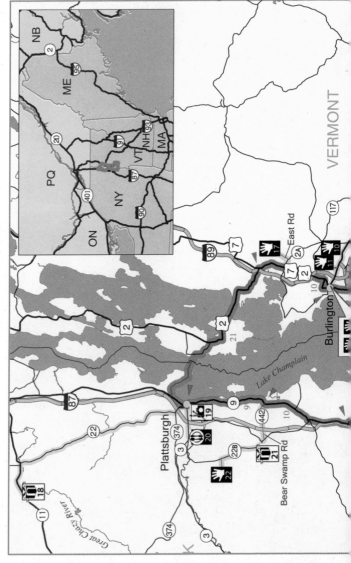

The main portion of the Lake Champlai

studio workshop

 craft marketplace

 special attraction

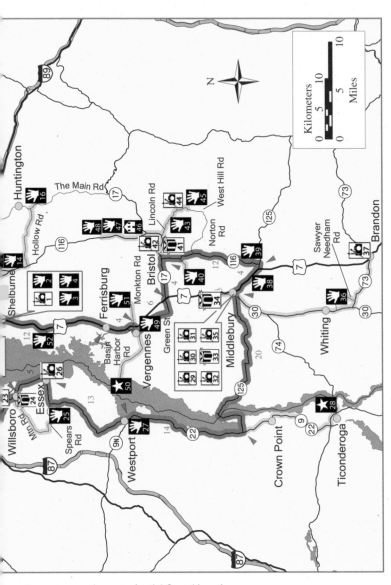

op is approximately 160 miles long.

SHELBURNE

Shelburne Craft School & Gallery

 Immerse yourself in American folk art from all angles— paintings, decorative arts, crafts, architecture, and artifacts. Thirty-nine buildings on forty-five acres house collections and permanent changing exhibitions. The School has been a resource for art and craft in the community since 1945 and classes are held in woodworking, ceramics, fiber arts, stained glass, and fine arts. Resident artists work in their studios producing work that is exhibited and sold nationally. At the school's Gallery on the Green, located in a fifth historic building, fine crafts made in Vermont and other parts of the US are showcased. The gallery also hosts fine art exhibits, talks, and poetry readings.

Studio open daily. Gallery closed on Sunday.

802-985-3648, 64 Harbor Road (studio), 54 Falls Road (gallery), Shelburne VT • www.shelburnecraftschool.org

TJF Turnings, LLC

 The large double-hung garage doors open onto this workshop, where a variety of functional and artistic lathe turned bowls and flatware in all sizes are carefully shaped.

Open year-round by appointment.

802-985 -2923 • 136 Davis Avenue, Shelburne, VT finkhaus@together.net

Beeken Parsons

 Furniture created by Bruce Beeken and Jeff Parsons celebrates wood. Each piece tells the story of a tree from forest to workshop and reflects Bruce and Jeff's commitment to sustainable forestry, dedication to craftsmanship, and thoughtful design. Their signature "Character wood" ™

 lodging restaurant artist gallery

Champlain Bikeways

The gentle, rolling hills that border Lake Champlain are perfect terrain for bicyclists, and the 363-mile Champlain Bikeway with its network of connecting theme loops offers opportunities for all levels of cycling experience. Try an overnight ride, string together several days exploring the lake islands, or follow the circuit around the entire lake. The wide roads and open terrain make this area a favorite for families and distance cyclists alike. Look for the Lake Champlain Bikeways Map and Guide, 3rd Edition *at local sports stores and recreation areas.*

Burlington bikepath in winter

features heartwood, sapwood, and mineral streaks. "We highlight rather than eliminate these characteristics; they give our furniture soul."

Open May–October Saturdays 10 am–4 pm and by appointment.

802-985-2913 · 1611 Harbor Road, Shelburne Farms, Shelburne, VT · info@beekenparsons.com

Turn into the Shelburne Farms property on the left, Harbor Rd. Workshop is in the southwest corner of the farm barn on the courtyard level; showroom is above.

Baynham Wood Products

Bill Baynham crafts his signature "Vermont Rocking Bear" from native Vermont hardwoods—red oak for the body, maple for the snout, and black walnut for the eyes and nose—and hand rubbed for a natural shine.

Open daily June–August.

802-985-9311 · 8 McDonald Farm Road, Shelburne, VT www.Baynhamwoodproducts.com

Second building on the right on McDonald Farm Road.

Chiroptera Cabin Company

In his garage, Barry Genzlinger makes wooden bat houses and sells a wide variety of books, videos, and posters on bats. Call to set up a demonstration!

Open year-round. Call for hours.

802-951-2501· 80 Black Lantern Lane, South Burlington, VT
www.chiropteracabins.com

From Shelburne, continue North on Rt. 7. Turn Right onto Laurel Hill Dr. Right at the fork. Continue straight onto Black Lantern Lane.

Church & Maple Glass Studio

Bud Shriner and his team of glassblowers breathe form and color into ethereal functional pieces with a modern aesthetic. This large industrial workshop has three furnaces—glory holes—that heat up to 2000 degrees, two kilns, annealing ovens, and a murrhini station. Emerging from these fires are graceful vases, bowls, platters, cake plates, and glasses. Fused mirrors, frames, and ornaments are also created on location.

Open Monday–Saturday 9 am–5 pm.

802-863-3880 · 225 Church Street, Burlington, VT
www.churchandmaple.com

Church Street is a pedestrian mall. Park your car and walk to #6-9

lodging restaurant artist gallery

Bright Moments

As a 5th generation Vermonter, Alicia LaVigne's quilt designs are influenced by the rural surroundings and a connection to quilters past and present. "I love to experiment with color . . . the often unpredictable results are reminiscent of natural patterns found in water, wood and clouds."

Open daily by chance or appointment.

802-734-4749
The Wing Building (next to Union Station), Suite 210,
Burlington, VT · brightmoments@together.net

Danforth Pewterers

Located in the old Blacksmith Shop of the Marble Works, the shop showcases the full line of handcrafted pewter oil lamps, candlesticks, bowls, vases, picture frames, key rings, jewelry, holiday ornaments, and baby items. View a pictorial exhibition of the pewter making process using 19th-century spinning lathes and 21st-century techniques. Also on display is a selection of antique pewter made by Fred Danforth's colonial American ancestors.

Open May–December: Monday–Saturday 10 pm–5 pm, Sunday 11 am–4 pm. Closed Sundays January–Memorial Day.

802-860-7135 · 111 Church Street, Burlington, VT
www.danforthpewter.com

 studio workshop

 craft marketplace

 special attraction

Frog Hollow Vermont State Craft Center

The variety and vision of Vermont artisans is the heart and soul of this contemporary gallery on Burlington's bustling pedestrian mall. Also a non-profit visual arts organization, Frog Hollow's mission is to "develop and strengthen the vibrant connection to the creation, appreciation, and support of fine Vermont craft through education, sales, and exhibition." A second gallery is located in Middlebury.

Open Monday–Saturday 10 am–6 pm, Sunday 12 noon–5 pm, Thanksgiving–Christmas: Monday–Saturday 10 am–9 pm, Sunday 12 noon–5 pm.

802-863-6458 • 85 Church Street, Burlington, VT
www.froghollow.org

Knotty Professor

These Celtic and Folk Harps are beautiful to behold and hear. Find a 36-string Celtic Harp and a 24-string Folk Harp at this studio, as well as the elegant accompaniments of music stands in maple and mahogany.

Open daily.

802-862-2240 • 78 Suburban Square, South Burlington, VT
www.KnottyProfessorOnLine.com

From Burlington, head East on Rt. 2. Turn left onto White St. and right into Suburban Square. Take the first left onto the North/East leg of the square.

Wood U Believe

Stop by this cozy shop to find Bob Bouvier building custom furniture, toy, craft, and wood items. His specialty is Early

American and Shaker and his Shaker oval boxes make great gifts! "I like clean lines and solid joinery."

Open year-round. Call for hours.

802-863-5644 • 26 Airport Parkway, South Burlington, VT
www.woodubelieve.com

From Suburban Square, turn right onto White St. Turn left onto Airport Parkway. Look for number on mailbox.

lodging   restaurant   artist gallery

Brian Jones Woodworking

At any time, Brian Jones has several custom projects in progress—chairs, tables, beds, or built-in cabinets. Stop by to watch wood turned into furniture or view his diverse portfolio.

Call for hours.

802-878-4895 · 73 Highlands Drive, Williston, VT
www.brianjoneswoodworking.com

Continue on Rt. 2 east. Turn left onto Rt. 2A south. Turn left onto Old Creamery Rd., then left onto Highlands Dr. First property on the left.

Paul's Woodworking

Think small when you enter this studio of doll furniture for the American Doll, including cradles, beds, bunk beds, armoires, and bureaus with a tilting mirror. Paul Lascelles works with Vermont pine and leaves all pieces unfinished.

Open daily 8 am–5 pm, call ahead.

802-879-7694
11 Ridge Road, Williston, VT

Continue south on Rt. 2A. Ridge Rd. is on the left across from the Seventh Day Adventist Church. Look for number on mailbox.

Russ Keil, Woodworker

From his home in this forested town, Russ Keil makes contemporary tables, lamps, boxes, and sculptures of mostly Vermont hardwoods.

Open year-round, daily during summer. Call for hours.

802-482-2237
104 Ayer Road, St. George, VT
rrkeil@adelphia.net

Continue South on Rt. 2A. Turn left onto Ayer Rd. Look for number on mailbox.

 studio workshop

 craft marketplace

 special attraction

Willow Pond Farm Bed & Breakfast

15

This farm's 200 acres of pasture, woods and meadows is surrounded on all sides by working farms and breathtaking Adirondack and Green Mountain views. Bordering Shelburne Pond, it is a haven for wildflowers, birds, and wildlife and the house is set among apple trees and romantic rose and perennial gardens. Three

guest rooms are furnished with antiques, handmade quilts, and oriental rugs. A full country breakfast is served in the dining area or out on the terrace under the pergola, among roses and honeysuckles.

Open year-round. Call for holiday schedule, Minimum 2 nights stay.

802-985-8505 • 133 Cheesefactory Lane, Shelburne, VT
www.virtualcities.com/vt/willow.htm

From Rt. 2A South, turn right onto Rt. 116 North. Turn left onto Cheesefactory Rd. Turn left onto Cheesefactory Lane.

A Confederate Raid in Vermont

In 1864, St. Albans, Vermont, was raided by a small group of Confederate soldiers in the most northerly attack of the Civil War. On Wednesday, October 19, 22 rebel soldiers quietly positioned themselves among the townspeople in preparation for their carefully orchestrated maneuver. At exactly 3 pm, some of the soldiers robbed the town's three banks while their partners herded the locals onto the village green. The conspirators escaped with over $200,000 and headed north for the Canadian border—only to be apprehended later. Today, the St. Albans Historical Society Museum displays some of the bills stolen during the action in remembrance of the day the Civil War came to Vermont.

 lodging   restaurant   artist gallery

Huntington River Smithy

Care and attention to detail define the contemporary ironwork of blacksmith James Fecteau, who uses forging methods dating back to the 14th century.

Open Monday–Wednesday 9 am–5 pm.

802-434-3871 · 1735 Main Road, Huntington, VT

From Rt. 2A South, turn left onto Hollow Rd., toward Huntington. Turn left onto Main Rd. Smithy is on the left, past the village of Huntington.

R. Henson Handcrafted Furniture

A juried member of the League of Vermont Furniture Makers, Randall Henson forms graceful and durable Windsor Chairs and furniture in his small workshop. The process includes steambending, legs turned on a lathe by hand, milk paint,

 and riving shaving. The finished piece symbolizes generations of North Country woodworkers and invites years of future use.

Open daily 8 am–5 pm.

802-878-6149
1276 East Road, Colchester, VT
www.randallhenson.com

Continue on Rt. 2 west/Rt. 7 north. Turn right onto Rte 2A. In Colchester Village, turn left onto East Rd. Shop is 1.2 miles down on the right.

Adirondack Pine

Located on the Great Chazy River, visitors will find a range of furniture at this shop. Knotty pine chests, traditional Adirondack fan-back chairs and love seats, child-size and doll-size Adirondack chairs, wooden rocking horses, and boxes for birds, bats, bugs, and butterflies are constructed from native white pine. Each piece is individually cut, sanded,

and assembled by hand using galvanized screws and bolts and then stained to customer preference.

Open daily April–December 8 am–5 pm.

518-236-7161 • 2973 Rt. 11, Mooers Forks, NY
www.adirondackpine.com

North Country Cultural Center

This art center, located in a former bank with vaulted 40-foot ceiling and generous windows, exhibits the works of 400 area artists on a rotating basis. Gift shop displays notecards, prints, pottery, and sculpture. Join for concerts, bridge, yoga, and life drawing classes.

Open Tuesday–Saturday 11 am–4 pm.

518-563-1604 • 30 Brinkerhoff Street, Plattsburgh, NY
www.nccca.org

Anthony's Restaurant & Bistro

Bring your hunger to this café for continental and American restaurant featuring local artists watercolors and oils.

Open for lunch: Monday–Friday 11:30 am–2:30 pm, dinner: daily 4 pm–7 pm.

518-561-6420 • 538 Rt. 3, Plattsburgh, NY

EXCURSION TO PERU AND MORRISONVILLE

A Poor Man's Collectibles

Stop by for rustic white birch frames, dressers, tables, lamps, desks, bookcases, signs, trunks, and boxes. Steve, owner and builder, welcomes custom orders.

Open daily 8 am–6 pm.

518-643-2016 • 3023 Main Street, Rt. 22, Peru, NY

Follow Rt. 442/Bear Swamp Rd. west to Peru.

If you were to walk around the entire shoreline of Lake Champlain, you would travel over 500 miles around the largest fresh water lake in the United States—excluding the Great Lakes.

Tidbits

 lodging restaurant   artist gallery

The Adirondack Woodturner

Kenneth Gadway turns natural-edge burl bowls and hollow forms on his lathe. Choose your fancy from traditional salad bowls to many sizes of bowls from a variety of Adirondack hardwoods. These works are often displayed in juried gallery exhibits around the region.

Open Monday–Thursday 8 am–3 pm or by appointment.
Summer: closed Wednesdays.

518-643-8427
169 Turner Road, Morrisonville, NY
adirondackwoodturner@yahoo.com

Follow Rt. 22B north to Morrisonville.
Retrace your steps to return to the main loop.

Willsboro Pharmacy

Stop in for toothpaste, a band-aid, or to browse the large selection of Adirondack books and gifts. Also find handknit baby sweaters, pottery, framed pictures, Adirondack posters and cards, party goods, gourmet foods, local maple products, handcrafted jewelry, candy, frames, dolls, and wind chimes. The Small Museum of Pharmacy has hundreds of mid-19th-century patent medicine bottles, cabinetry, prescriptions, and reference books. Solar panels on roof provide the giftshop's lighting. Try to catch the periodic book signings!

Open weekdays 9 am–5:30 pm, Saturday 9 am–5 pm, Sunday 9 am–2 pm.

518-963-8946 · 62 Station Road, Willsboro, NY
dick@deneale.com

Cornerstone

A gem on the hillside, this elegant church was built in 1902 but desanctified in the 1950s. Lovingly restored to its original glow, it is now a space for creative and spiritual renewal, featuring exquisite pieces of rustic furniture and accessories, made by Adirondack artisans. The name refers to a time capsule that was placed in the cornerstone of the building and can only be opened by the Episcopal Diocese of Albany.

Open April–December, Thursday–Saturday, 12 noon–5 pm.

518-873-6788 · 17 Maple Street (at Rt. 22), Willsboro, NY
www.cedarvale.com/cs/

 studio workshop

 craft marketplace

 special attraction

EXCURSION

Alice Wand—Studio & Gallery

Alice Wand creates unusual 2-dimensional "textured landscapes" composed of handmade paper, acrylic paint, and digital photography. Visitors to her working studio can view her framed work on display.

Open June–August, Thanksgiving–Christmas: Saturday–Sunday 1 pm–5 pm.

518-963-4582
44 Spear Road,
Willsboro, NY
www.alicewand.com

Cupola House Gallery and Still Hollow Miniature Quilts

This gallery houses owner Donna Lou Sonnett's collection of folk art, fine art, quilts, and primitives by eight local artists, as well as vintage work. "Still Hollow Miniature Quilts"—traditionally pieced and hand quilted on site—are permanently displayed at the Cupola House Gallery.

Open Friday–Sunday 12 noon–5 pm.

518-963-7494 • South Main Street, Essex, NY
cupolahouse@hotmail.com

Westport Trading Company

For over a quarter century, stained glass artist Kip Trienens has been producing brilliant panels of glass for the home, office, and camp. His work in church restoration and hand beveling of glass is done at this studio. Amidst the rich colors of the glass are Inuit stone carvings, Yoruba door panels, jewelry from Nepal, Mexico, and Morroco and works from regional artists.

Open year-round. Call for hours.

518-962-4801 • 6511 North Main Street, Westport, NY

lodging   restaurant   artist gallery

EXCURSION TO TICONDEROGA

Fort Ticonderoga

Overlooking Lake Champlain, Fort Ticonderoga was the scene of major battles and military maneuvers in the French and Indian War and American Revolution. Its buildings, exhibits, and grounds interpret historical events and the lives of soldiers at the fort. Wander the restored "King's Garden," and recreated Native American and garrison gardens or visit the museum, store, or restaurant. The Fort hosts several reenactments each season.

Open May–October: daily 9 am–5 pm.
Partially handicapped accessible.

518-585-2821 · Fort Road at NY Rt. 74, Ticonderoga, NY

Henry Sheldon Museum of Vermont History

A brick Federal-style home built by local marble merchants in 1829, this elegant house has six fireplaces of rare black marble mined nearby in Shoreham. The museum's collections include thousands of documents, letters, and photographs collected by Henry Sheldon that present an intimate portrait of local life during the 1800s. Among the textiles, glass, paintings, tools, and musical instruments, are examples of furniture by local cabinetmakers, Hastings Warren and Dexter Derby; using many of the same woods Vermont cabinetmakers work with today; pine, figured maple, and cherry. Ask for the Sheldon's Vermont Furniture Guide when you tour the museum.

Open Monday–Saturday 10 am–5 pm.
November–May, closed Mondays. $5 Adult, $4.50 Senior, $3 Youth (6–18), free under six.

802-388-2117 · 1 Park Street, Middlebury, VT
info@henrysheldonmuseum.org

Henry Sheldon Museum of Vermont History

 studio workshop  craft marketplace   special attraction

Otter Creek Craft Gallery

An inviting mix of handmade crafts from nationally recognized artists makes this space magical. Bob Crystal throws all the stoneware pottery. Find jewelry, clay masks, wooden bowls, and much more.

Open Summer–Fall: Monday–Saturday 11 am–5 pm, Winter: Tuesday–Saturday 12 noon–5 pm.

802-388-2344 • 5 Park Street, Middlebury, VT
www.robertcrystalpottery.com

Frog Hollow Vermont State Craft Center

Enter this old mill that has been stylishly recast as a contemporary gallery overlooking Otter Creek. Alive with a collection of fine craft from 225 juried Vermont artisans, the gallery supports the non-profit mission of this visual arts organization. See location listing in Burlington also.

Open daily.

802-388-3177 • 1 Mill Street, Middlebury, VT
www.froghollow.org

Holy Cow, Inc.

Best known for the black and white Holsteins that graze peacefully on Ben & Jerry's Ice Cream containers, Woody Jackson's gallery and shop features his original paintings and prints.

Open May–December: Monday– Saturday 9 am–5 pm, Sunday 12 noon–5 pm, January–April: Tuesday–Saturday 10 am–5 pm.

802-388-6737 • 44 Main Street, Middlebury, VT

Danforth Pewterers

See listing earlier in this chapter for Danforth Pewterers in Burlington.

802-388-0098 • 211 Maple Street, The Marble Works, Middlebury, VT • www.danforthpewter.com

 lodging   restaurant   artist gallery

Fisk Quarry

A wetland wildlife habitat that's home to birds, fish, and colorful wildflowers, Fisk Quarry offers a rare snapshot of the world as it was half a billion years ago. This little-known site contains the oldest exposed fossilized coral reef in the world, dating back some 480 million years. Just as Vesuvius' lava preserved the frescos of Pompeii, centuries of ocean sediment (yes, this once was the ocean floor) preserved the fossils of extinct sponges, tube coral, and ancestors of starfish that can now be seen forever frozen in limestone. To visit this unique site, follow Rt. 2 west through Lake Champlain's northern islands, take a left on Route 129, and follow this road until you see the Fisk Quarry sign and a small gravel parking lot on your right.

Vermont Soapworks

Sweet smells waft through the entryway . . . let your nose lead the way inside. This small company produces a full line of handmade aromatherapy bar soaps, on display in handmade wooden boxes and apple baskets. Also available is a collection of antique soap-making equipment. Call to schedule a tour.

Open Monday–Friday 9 am–5 pm,
Saturday 10 am–4 pm, Sunday 11 am–4 pm.
Closed Sundays Christmas–Memorial Day.

866-762-7482 · 616 Exchange Street, Middlebury, VT
www.vtsoap.com

Vermont Folklife Center

This gallery space with changing exhibits and store chock-full of crafts by Vermont artisans is heaven for the folk art lover! Featured traditional crafts reflect a diversity of styles, resources, and influences. Find Native American baskets, ornaments, whirligigs, handknit clothing, brooms, wooden spoons and bowls, hooked and braided rugs, handcarved objects, tramp art, homemade soap, and beeswax candles.

 studio workshop

 craft marketplace

 special attraction

Local stories come alive through a collection of recordings and books featuring conversations with Vermonters and others from the region.

Open June–November: Tuesday–Saturday 10 am–4 pm, December: daily 10 am–5 pm, January–May: Thursday–Saturday 10–4 pm.

802-388-4964 • 3 Court Street, Middlebury, VT
www.vermontfolklifecenter.org

EXCURSION TO WHITING AND BANDON

Cotswold Furniture Makers

In this former dairy barn converted to a workshop, John Lomas designs and six skilled craftsmen build Shaker-inspired, furniture for the home and office. Since 2004, Cotswold has used at least 70% sustainably harvested lumber. "Our guiding principle is simple: The use of top quality hardwood lumber, modern tools, and equipment and traditional joinery techniques, guarantee the integrity of each piece for life."

Open year-round by appointment.

802-623-8400 • 904 Sawyer-Needham Rd, Whiting, VT
www.cotswoldfurniture.com

Turn left onto Sawyer-Needham Rd. from Rt. 73 East. Look for the large red barn on the right.

Warren Kimble Gallery

For that New England feel, there is nothing like Warren Kimble's stylized compositions of animals and farm scenes. Although his studio is no longer open to the public, local galleries carry his work.

   lodging restaurant artist gallery

Champ: The Local Sea Monster

On Perkins Pier in Burlington a granite marker is dedicated to Champ, Lake Champlain's mysterious sea monster. According to local legend, as early as 1609 French explorer Samuel de Champlain claimed to have seen a "20 foot serpent thick as a barrel with a head like a horse." Local Indians probably knew about the creature long before, and sightings have continued through the centuries and into the present. Some claim that Champ is a giant lake sturgeon, others that it is a plesiosaur, the same prehistoric species often proposed as the true identity of the Loch Ness Monster. A "Champ Sightings Board," located at the southern entrance to Port Henry on Route 9N, tracks the names of people who have seen Champlain's monster. Keep your eyes peeled, and maybe you can add your name to the list.

Lock-n-Glass Crafters

Stained glass windows, lampshades, panels, and sun catchers are Dennis Cassidy's specialty.

Open Monday–Thursday 7:30 am–9 am, 3 pm–5 pm, Friday 7:30 am–5 pm, Saturday 8 am–4 pm.

802-388-7633 · 1590 Rt. 7 South, Middlebury, VT

Edward L. Allen, Furnituremaker

Find this shop and showroom at the end of a dirt road against a wild backdrop of a wetland and the Green Mountains. Edward Allen produces fine furniture ranging from quilt racks and mirrors to desks, tables, and dressers using native hardwoods, especially black cherry. Influenced by a Shaker aesthetic—clean lines and classic proportions—he uses traditional joinery, including dovetailing and pegged mortise and tenons and hand-rubs an oil finish to a smooth, satin surface.

 studio workshop

 craft marketplace

 special attraction

Open daily by chance or appointment.

**802-388-9274 • 6 South Leno Lane, Middlebury, VT
edwardallen@adelphia.net**

Head north on Rt. 116. Turn right onto North Leno Lane, and bear right onto South Leno Lane.

Lucarelli Woodworks

In a bucolic setting with views of South Mountain and adjacent to a 100-tap sugarbush, this cabinet and furniture shop is a must see! Ben Lucarelli uses traditional methods and design to create pieces made to last and exhibits milling, joining, and finishing.

Open year-round. Call for hours.

**802-453-5021 • 823 Sumner Road, New Haven, VT
benlucarelli@hotmail.com**

Continue north on Rt. 116 for several miles. Turn left onto Cove Rd., then left onto River Rd., and right onto Sumner Rd. Travel one mile, all the way to the top of the hill.

Vermont Honey Lights

Open the door to this retail shop and experience the sweet scent of beeswax. Candles are poured into works of art of all shapes, sizes, and color. Visitors can shop for vintage accents and home furnishings or enter the garden gates to view production. Just ask one of the four owners why beeswax is the best to burn!

Open Monday–Friday 9am–5 pm, Saturday 10 am–4 pm, Sunday (October through December) 11am–4 pm.

**802-453-3952 • 9 Main Street, Bristol, VT
www.vermonthoneylights.com**

Art on Main

A magnet for the creative, this gallery featuring 110 artists—almost half who live in the five-town area of Bristol—represent all media. See the Artists' Alley at the entrance, where five benches and five murals painted by 6th grade students depict local spirit.

Open Monday–Saturday 10 am–6 pm, Sunday 12 noon–5 pm. Call for winter hours.

**802-453-4032 • 25C Main Street, Artists' Alley, Bristol, VT
www.artonmain.net**

 lodging   restaurant   artist gallery

Lincoln Pottery

Judith Bryant's distinctive wheel-thrown pottery is made in this old dairy barn.

Open daily 12 noon–5 pm. Closed holidays.

802-453-2073 · 220 West River Road, Lincoln, VT
brymarsh@sover.net

Leaving Bristol, continue on Rt. 17 East. Turn right onto Lincoln Rd. This turns into West River Rd in Lincoln.

Prescott Galleries

Reed Prescott is one of New England's premier nature painters and illustrators. His landscapes and wildlife studies have been shown in galleries across the northeast. When he is not at work in his studio, he might be wandering the lovely grounds and gardens.

Open Tuesday, Friday, Saturday, 10 am–5 pm
and by appointment.

802-453-4776 · 47 East River Road, Lincoln, VT
www.prescottgalleries.com

The West River Rd. turns into the East River Rd.

Vermont Heritage Woodworks

Situated on 80 acres of open fields with a dramatic view of Mt. Abraham and the Green Mountains, Stephen Taylor works in a restored Clayton Baslow barn built by his great grandfather in 1917. He makes furniture, cabinets, and woodenware using traditional methods and wood from his land. "We have 200 acres of woodland in active production, all certified sustainable by the Forest Stewardship Council." The barn also houses a showroom featuring diverse work by local woodworkers who emphasize the use of certified lumber. Schedule a demonstration or educational tour on the basic principles of sustainable forestry, low impact harvesting, lumber making, and woodworking.

 studio
workshop

 craft
marketplace

 special
attraction

Open by appointment or schedule a demonstration in September–October.

802-453-3225 · 716 West Hill Road, Lincoln, VT
vhw@gmavt.net

From the Lincoln General Store (where West River Rd. becomes East River Rd.), cross the bridge directly opposite the store. This is Gore Hill Rd. Bear left at the fork onto West Hill Rd. Continue 0.7 mile to the large barn on the left.

The Inn at Baldwin Creek and Mary's Restaurant

Perennial flower, herb and vegetable gardens, and the rushing Baldwin Creek surround this quaint inn, creating an intimate, quintessential Vermont retreat. The inn's chef-owned restaurant is known for changing menus each season and highlighting local farm products. The Cream of Garlic Soup is world famous and the gourmet breakfast includes homemade blackberry jam. Original Farmhouse Dinners are co-hosted by the inn's farm partners and exclusively offer locally produced foods.

Open for dinner Wednesdays July–August.

802-453-2432 · 1868 North Rt. 116, Bristol, VT
www.innatbaldwincreek.com

    lodging   restaurant   🖼 artist gallery

Robert Compton Pottery

Once a dairy farm, this series of buildings feature an eclectic mix of architecture. The studio boasts the greatest number and widest variety of kilns in New England: Two Japanese style, "Noborigama" two-chambered kilns; a single-chambered, wood-fired, salt kiln; two Raku kilns; a gas-fired car kiln and a primitive pit kiln. Robert Compton's pottery ranges from petite porcelain tea bowls to oversized urns reminiscent of Greek amphora pots. Also on display are hanging stoneware aquariums and 6-foot tall porcelain

waterfalls. Christine, Robert's wife, is an accomplished weaver and spinner and her chenille scarves and shawls are on display in the showroom.

Open mid-May–mid-October: Thursday–Tuesday 10 am–6 pm.

802-453-3778 • 2662 Rt. 116 North, Bristol, VT
www.RobertComptonPottery.com

Open Studio Weekend

Vermont Open Studio Weekend is held each year on Memorial Day Weekend. This statewide event is an opportunity to step inside the workspaces of more than 200 artists and craftspeople, including sculptors, potters, glass blowers, blacksmiths, painters, woodworkers, and weavers. Many of these artists open their studios to visitors only during this event or by appointment. Open Studio Weekend was launched in 1992 to invite the public into the environment where craft is produced. Information and a map of participating studios are available from the Vermont Crafts Council, PO Box 938, Montpelier, VT 05601; or by calling (802) 223-3380. For more details, see the VT Crafts Council Web site: www.vermontcrafts.com.

 studio workshop   craft marketplace special attraction

Vermont Folk Rocker

48 Just a few minutes in one of these exceptionally comfortable rocking chair will make the visit worthwhile. Jim Geier has been making durable and elegant chairs since 1974 out of native hardwoods—cherry, red oak, birdseye maple, and black walnut—finished in non-toxic linseed oil.

Open year-round.
Call for hours.

802-453-2483
3820 Rt. 116, Starksboro, VT
www.vermontfolkrocker.com

Robert Popick Studio & Frame Shop

49 In this 19th-century barn that serves as a studio, Robert Popick creates original watercolors, oils, and prints featuring landscapes of Vermont and New England. His fine framing uses Vermont hardwood and other styles.

Open Thursday–Saturday 10 am–5 pm or by appointment.

802-877-3323 • 498 Rt. 66, Waltham, VT

Continue West on Rt. 17 to Waltham. Turn right onto Green St. Turn left onto Rt. 66. No sign—look for the large barn.

 lodging restaurant artist gallery

EXCURSION TO VERGENNES

Lake Champlain Maritime Museum

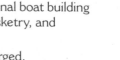

Vermont's rich maritime heritage is brought to life through a large collection of original small watercraft built in the region over the past 150 years. Watch boat building in progress in the modern Boat Shop. Or learn the art of traditional boat building and maritime related crafts, blacksmithing, basketry, and photography in workshops.

Open daily May–mid-October. Admission charged.

802-475-2022 • 4472 Basin Harbor Road, Vergennes, VT
www.lcmm.org

Continue up Green St. toward Vergennes. In downtown Vergennes, turn left onto Rt. 22A. Turn right onto Panton Rd. then right onto Basin Harbor Rd.

Black & White and Color

Judith and Denis Versweyveld find beauty in simple forms. Visitors to their studio can find original acrylic and oil paintings as well as sculpture in bronze, plaster, and cement.

Open May–October: Monday–Friday 11 pm–4 pm. Call ahead.

802-877-2526 • 3367 Monkton Road, Vergennes, VT
www.blackwhiteandcolor.com

Look for number on mailbox.

Adirondack Guideboat, Inc.

A classic Northern Forest symbol of outdoor recreation, Adirondack guideboats by David Rosen and his team are designed and built in traditional cedar, pine, cherry, and spruce.

Kevlar and fiberglass versions with cherry trim and oars and original Vermont Packboats are also on display.

Open weekdays 8 am–5 pm. Weekends by appointment.

802-425-3926
Rt. 7, North Ferrisburgh, VT
www.adirondack-guide-boat.com

 studio workshop

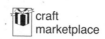 craft marketplace

 special attraction

107

Chapter
6

Capital & Country

From a legendary puppet museum to the heart of Vermont's ski country to the vibrant state capitol, Vermont's northern Green Mountains are home to a fascinating array of cultural, scenic, and historic destinations. Playwright David Mamet, who lived in northern Vermont for nearly 40 years, once described people of this region as "practitioners of the old home crafts."

Vermont Capitol building

The Capital and Country Tour is anchored by Montpelier—the smallest capital city in the country, but one of the most bustling. While you're in town, visit the gold-domed capitol building or the nearby Vermont Historical Society museum. Heading east out of town and then north, and you'll pass through classic Vermont dairy country and the home of the famous Cabot Creamery.

From the country crossroads in Hardwick, take your pick from two routes northward. One offers a chance to shop and enjoy picturesque Craftsbury Common. The other provides the opportunity to explore the Bread and Puppet Museum and its kaleidoscope of giant, handmade puppets. To avoid the hard decision, you may want to simply take the time to travel both routes.

From Irasburg, after a side trip to Derby or Newport along the shores of Lake Memphremagog, head west to Johnson for a stroll through the grounds of the largest artists' community in the United States—the Vermont Studio Center. From here you'll head south again, through the heart of the northern Green Mountains, and the shadow of Vermont's tallest peak, 4,393-foot Mount Mansfield.

In Stowe, stop to visit the local sculpture garden or furniture workshop, then head over to the base of the mountain to visit the Trapp Family Lodge, established by the von Trapp family of *The Sound of Music* fame. Continuing south, cross Interstate 89 and head into the Mad River Valley for stops in Waitsfield and Morrisville before rounding out your trip back in busy Montpelier.

Cultural Heritage Profile

Alexander Twilight and the Old Stone House

The Old Stone House in Brownington, Vermont, stands as a testament to one of the nation's pioneering African Americans.

Born in 1795, Alexander Twilight was the first African American to earn a college degree at an American institution. He earned his degree from Middlebury College in 1823. According to records at the Vermont Historical Society, Twilight moved to Brownington in 1829, where he took up the duties of both pastor and teacher. Faced with a growing student enrollment, Twilight designed and oversaw the construction of a four-story, stone school building and the expansion of Orleans County Grammar School as Brownington Academy. He called his massive building Athenian

Photo by: Jerry & Marcy Monkman/EcoPhotography.com

Painting from the Old Stone House Museum

Hall. Today it is known simply as the Old Stone House.

In 1836 and 1837, Twilight was elected to the General Assembly, becoming the first African American to serve as a Vermont state representative. Twilight died in 1857 after spending his later years supervising the education of students at his academy. He is buried with his wife in the Brownington churchyard, within sight of the stone schoolhouse he built and directed.

Now home to the Orleans County Historical Society, the Old Stone House Museum complex includes five historic 19th-century structures and 55 acres of field and pasture. Exhibits include handmade objects reflecting life in rural Vermont from the late 18th through early 20th centuries, including furniture, textiles, quilts, hooked and braided rugs, baskets, pottery, handmade tools, and folk art.

The Museum Shop features traditional handcrafts made by local artisans. Each year, the museum hosts Heritage Craft Workshops in July, and a Holiday Craft Workshop in November. Traditional crafts also are demonstrated at public events including Old Stone House Day each August.

See the listing on page 127 for contact information.

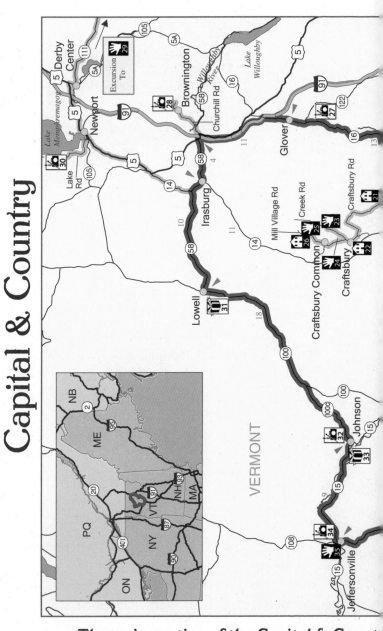

The main portion of the Capital & Count

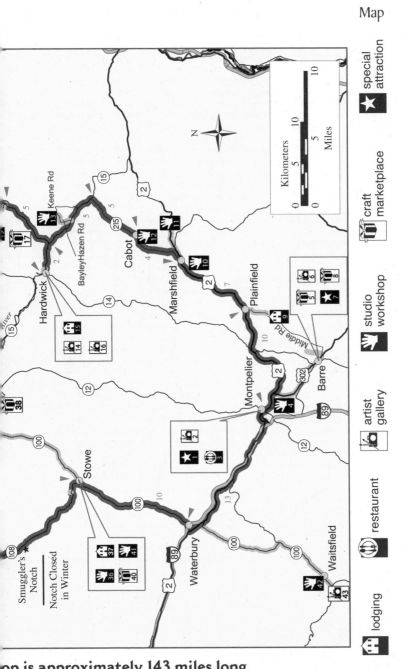

special attraction

craft marketplace

studio workshop

artist gallery

restaurant

lodging

Keene Rd

15

2

13

17

BayleyHazen Rd

5

215

5

12

11

Cabot

4

10

Marshfield

2

7

Plainfield

Middle Rd

10

6

8

5

7

9

14

Hardwick

River

15

15

14

Montpelier

2

302

Barre

12

2

38

4

89

12

100

Stowe

2

1

3

100

10

13

108

Smuggler's Notch

Notch Closed in Winter

37

41

36

40

100

89

Waterbury

2

100

Waitsfield

100

42

43

N

Kilometers

0   5   10

Miles

0   5   10

op is approximately 143 miles long.

113

MONTPELIER

Open Studio Weekend
Vermont Craft Council

Step inside the workspaces of more than 200 sculptors, glass blowers, blacksmiths, painters, woodworkers, jewelers, and weavers across the state. This event was launched in 1992 to invite visitors into the environment where craft is produced and every year over 10,000 visitors meet the artisans, learn about the creative process and buy one-of-a-kind items.

Memorial Day Weekend.

802-223-3380
www.vermontcrafts.com

Artisans Hand

More than 120 Vermont crafts people are represented in this bright showroom in downtown Montpelier. Cooperatively owned by artisans for 25 years, the gallery exhibits traditional and contemporary craftwork. Feel free to ask questions about the creative process behind the exhibits because artisans staff the

gallery! Try to catch a craft demonstration, fashion show, or receptions.

Open Monday–Saturday
10 am–5:30 pm,
Friday 10 am–8 pm,
Sunday 12 noon–4 pm.
Call or visit our website for extended Holiday hours.

802-229-9492
89 Main Street,
Montpelier, VT
www.artisanshand.com

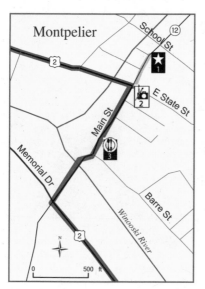

🏠 lodging   🍴 restaurant   📷 artist gallery

Only the Freshest Ingredients

The Vermont Fresh Network delivers just-harvested produce from local farms directly to restaurants throughout the state. Founded by a graduate of the New England Culinary Institute in Montpelier, the program enables more than 120 chefs to make informal agreements with over 100 farmers. The personal relationships between chef and farmer are demonstrated through delicious cheeses and preserves, meat and poultry, produce and cut flowers. Look for the VFN emblem in restaurants and cafés.

Rhapsody

Located in a historic building in downtown Montpelier, this cafe offers a self-serve natural food cafe featuring locally grown organic produce. Exhibits by local artists display traditional and contemporary arts and crafts.

Open Monday–Saturday 11:30 am–8:30 pm.

802-229-6112 · 28 Main Street, Montpelier, VT
www.rhapsodynaturalfoods.org

Vermont Weatherworks, LLC

Find weathervanes hand-carved and painted in sumptuous, life-like colors making them just as likely to be displayed within the home as on the roof. Designs include rainbow, brook and brown trout, striped and largemouth bass, and nine dog breeds in addition to whimsical and traditional subjects. Witness the construction of white pine doweled and glued for strength and stability, then covered with successive layers of exterior enamel paint and coated with premium marine spar varnish.

Open Monday–Friday 9 am–5 pm.

802-229-0269 · 3C Karl's Circle, Montpelier, VT
www.vtweatherworks.com

Approximately 0.75 miles east of the intersection of Rts. 2 and 302, on the right.

 studio workshop    craft marketplace   special attraction

EXCURSION TO BARRE

Vermont Outdoor Furniture

Creative comfort! This factory produces a full line of northern white cedar outdoor furniture.

 Open Monday–Friday 8:30 am–5 pm, and in May–September Saturday 10 am–5 pm.

800-588-8834 • 9 Auburn Street, Barre VT
www.vermontoutdoorfurniture.com

Located east of Montpelier, approximately 0.75 miles east of the intersection of Rts. 2 and 302. On right side of the road, large sign on front of light blue clapboard building.

Studio Place Arts (SPA)

Since opening its doors in 2000, this community center for the visual arts exudes creative energy throughout its historic downtown building. An important resource for art making, learning, and exhibition, there are innovative exhibits on 3 floors. Featuring regional, national, and international artists and artisans, visitors will find paintings, stone and clay sculpture, drawings, photography, lithography, fiber arts, and woodworking. Don't miss the stone art exhibit each October featuring the most compelling works of local stone carvers.

Open Tuesday–Friday 10 am–5 pm, Saturday 12 noon–4 pm.

802-479-7069 • 201 North Main Street, Barre, VT
www.studioplacearts.com

Hope Cemetery

When a wave of Italian immigrants made their way to America in the 19th century, many stonecutters came to Barre to work in the world's largest granite quarries. Some were masterful carvers, as evident in many marble sculptures scattered throughout town. Italy's legacy lives on in this cemetery. With its lyrical inscriptions and gleaming marble statuary "including

  lodging   restaurant   artist gallery

a replica of Michelangelo's Pieta" the Hope Cemetery ranks among America's finest. Where else can you find a married couple holding hands in bed, a half-sized stock car etched from white granite, or a rendering of the tractor-trailer that Uncle Nat drove up and down I-89? Wander around the newer section close to the entrance and you'll find a basketball,

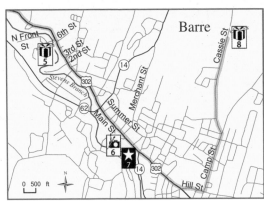

armchair, Civil Air Patrol plane, and perfect cube poised on its corner, each in some way emblematic of the diversity of life in this community.

Rt. 14, Barre, VT

Woodcarvers Depot

Wood carver aficionados welcome! Find custom woodcarving knives, specialty carving and marking tools, cut outs, blanks, and bases at this store. Don Heuerman also sells his work including Woodspirit hiking and walking sticks, exotic wood jewelry, Santa Claus and caricature figures, and cottonwood bark Woodspirits.

Open year-round by appointment.

802-479-9563
62 Cassie Street, Barre, VT
www.woodcarversdepot.com

From center of Barre, go east on Washington St./Rt. 302 to 1st light at top of hill. Turn left on Hill St., then left on Camp St. At top of hill turn left and go about 0.75 miles on Cassie St.

Handcrafted wooden canes

 studio workshop

 craft marketplace

 special attraction

117

StoneHead Farm Bed & Breakfast

Located on a quiet country road, this early 1800s farmhouse sits on 80 acres of rolling pastures and woods with dramatic views of Camel's Hump and the Green Mountains. As a comfortable refuge after a long day or traveling or a starting point for exploring the outdoors, these bright, Shaker-style rooms and homemade Dutch or American breakfast might be just the treat. Open January–March, July–October.

802-476-4273 • 2084 Middle Road, Plainfield, VT
www.StoneHeadFarm.com

Heading east on Rt. 2 to Plainfield, turn right at blinking light into Plainfield village. Turn right at the church on to Mill St., which changes into Barre Hill Rd., for 0.7 miles. Turn left at "Y" onto Middle Rd. for 2.1 miles. StoneHead Farm is on the right.

Blackthorne Forge

This versatile workshop resides in an old yellow dairy barn along the Winooski River. Blacksmith Steven Bronstein uses traditional and modern tools and techniques of this 3,000-year-old craft, to make functional and sculptural objects.

Open Monday–Saturday 9 am–3 pm. Call ahead.

802-426-3369 (office) • 802-426-4222 (studio)
247 Gilman Street, 3821 Rt. 2, Marshfield, VT
www.blackthorneforge.com

Schumacher Weathervanes

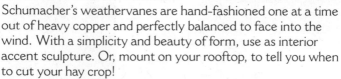

Weathervanes have shown the direction of the coming weather since the Middle Ages. It was not so long ago that the very survival of the community depended on knowing about the coming of storms or sunshine. Michael Schumacher's weathervanes are hand-fashioned one at a time out of heavy copper and perfectly balanced to face into the wind. With a simplicity and beauty of form, use as interior accent sculpture. Or, mount on your rooftop, to tell you when to cut your hay crop!

Open April–November: call ahead. December–March: weekdays 9 am–5 pm, Saturday 12 noon–5 pm.

802-426-3535 • 1380 Rt. 2, Marshfield, VT

 lodging restaurant artist gallery

Farms and Barns

The farms and barns of the Northern Forest remind us of an era when cows often outnumbered people in some areas—particularly here in north-central Vermont. Today, barns scattered across the region teach us about the people and practices that led to their design. Watch for these features and learn about the region's farming heritage. Here are some styles to look for:

• English Barns (1770s–1900s): The earliest colonial farmers built small barns—about 30 feet by 40 feet—with large, hinged doors on the long side and unpainted vertical boards on the walls. English barns usually stood on a level site with no basement.

• Yankee Barns (1820s–1870s): These barns were usually built into a hillside so manure could be pushed into a basement below. The entrance is on the end, and the siding is horizontal to keep the draft out. Rooftop ventilators for fresh air and windows for light are characteristic.

• Late Bank Barns (1870s–1900s): Huge multi-story bank barns, topped by a gabled roof and decorative cupola for ventilation, were built to house large herds of cattle and other livestock. At the uphill end, watch for a covered bridge or "high-drive" that allowed wagons to get to the upper hayloft.

• Round Barns (1899–1920): This design was meant to save labor, with all the cows facing into a central feeding point. The first round barn in Vermont was built in 1899 on what is now Route 5 in Barnet. It is used as storage space by the seventh generation of farmers to live and work the land on Round Barn Farm.

Hillside, Greensboro, VT

 studio
workshop

 craft
marketplace

 special
attraction

Vermont Floorcloths/Hillcrest Nursery

Sandy Ducharme makes canvas floorcloths using traditional and contemporary designs. This New England tradition originated along the seacoast as settlers stenciled patterns onto old sails and sealed the painted canvas with varnish. A stroll through the nursery in summer is a must.

Open daily May–October.

802-563-2745 • 849 Ducharme Road, Cabot, VT
vtfloorcloths@yahoo.com

In Marshfield Village, go north on Rt. 215 to Cabot, 2.5 miles. Turn left onto Ducharme Road and continue for 1 mile.

Watergate Forge

Fire and water fuse together in this blacksmith's forge where James Teuscher teaches the art of forging. His work includes furniture and functional art, as well as decorative pieces of all sizes. A walk through the fields leads to a private sculpture garden.

Call for an appointment.

802-563-2037 • 629 Keene Road, East Hardwick, VT

At intersection of Bayley-Hazen Rd. and Rt. 15 (South Walden) go north on Bayley-Hazen Rd., 0.9 miles to Keene Rd. on right. Go up Keene Rd. 0.6 miles to mailbox #629. Entrance to forge on left.

G.R.A.C.E.

Standing for Grassroots Art and Community Effort, G.R.A.C.E.'s permanent and consigned collections of contemporary self-taught art are on display in the old firehouse gallery. The collection features paintings, drawings, and mixed media products of the 25-year-old program, which brings art workshops and classes to institutions across Vermont. Don't miss one of the six rotating exhibitions or the open house in December!

Open Tuesday–Thursday 10 am–4 pm.

802-472-6857 • 13 Mill Street, Hardwick, VT

 lodging   restaurant   artist gallery

Somerset House B&B

On a quiet maple-lined avenue, visitors will find a comfortable

bed in this elegant 1890s Queen Anne-style house, recognized since 1998 as a Green Hotel by the State of Vermont for its environmentally friendly practices.

Open daily.

802-472-5484;
800-838-8074
130 Highland Avenue,
Hardwick, VT
www.somersethousebb.com

Hardwick Town House/
Northeast Kingdom Artisans Guild

Originally built as a primary school in 1860, this building was transformed into a first-rate opera house in the early 20th century, when a stage, seating, and balcony were installed. More recently, the Northeast Kingdom Arts Council has been restoring the Town House to its original splendor and the Craftsbury Chamber Players host their annual summer festival here. Ongoing programs and performances in film, drama, music, and dance are scheduled year-round and the second floor is a gallery displaying work by local artists. A unique Vermont tradition, the Town House has two painted curtains from the early 1900s by Charles W. Henry.

Open
Thursday–Saturday
10 am–3 pm.

802-472-8800
127 Church Street,
Hardwick, VT

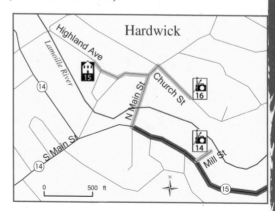

studio
workshop

craft
marketplace

special
attraction

121

Perennial Pleasures Nursery

17

An everlasting delight! The nursery specializes in old-fashioned, hardy perennial flowers and herbs. The gift shop is full of colorful quilts, pillows, tea cozies, potholders, dolls, clothes, and jewelry. Time your afternoon stops around tea, sandwiches, and cakes in the enchanted tea garden or green house!

Open June–September 10 am–5 pm. Closed Mondays.
Teatime: Memorial Day–Labor Day: 12 noon–5 pm.
Reservations are suggested.

802-472-5512 · 63 Brick House Road, East Hardwick, VT

New Wing Designs/Silver Wing Designs

18

Për Courtney specializes in 18th- and 19th-century furniture replicas and case pieces made in the best traditions of the old masters. He also builds custom furniture and cabinetry and the shop displays antique hand tools, still used to handcraft dovetails, carved fans and shells, and inlays. Visitors can also find his handcrafted silver jewelry in designs ranging from elegant to industrial. Tour the four acres of woodlands and gardens, cultivated by Lynette Courtney, a professional gardener.

Open year-round.
802-533-2444
281 The Bend Road,
Greensboro Bend, VT
www.newwingdesigns.com

Turn left onto Rt. 15,
The Bend Road.

lodging   restaurant   artist gallery

EXCURSION TO GREENSBORO, CRAFTSBURY AND CRAFTSBURY COMMON

Lakeview Inn & Restaurant

The Lakeview Inn started as a boarding house in 1872 attracting visitors in horse drawn carriages. Now a family-run inn listed on the National and Vermont Historic Registers, it makes the perfect end-of-the-day destination! In the restaurant, you can expect seasonally inspired, sophisticated American cuisine using the freshest local and artisan products available. Each dish is prepared to showcase the flavor and quality of the ingredients, a tribute to the farmers and growers of Vermont.

Open year round.

802-533-2291 or 888-251-0100
295 Breezy Avenue, Greensboro, VT 05841
www.lakeviewinn.biz

Caspian Hot Glass Studio

Glassblowers Jacob Barron and Lucas Lonengren demonstrate their art in this bright studio built to resemble a sugarhouse. The connected gallery displays their delicate and original glass lighting and tableware—bowls, glasses, pitchers, plates—as well as ornaments and unique creations.

Open daily 10 am–5 pm.

802-533-7129 • Top of Breezy Avenue, Greensboro, VT
www.caspianglass.com

Highland Lodge

This elegant lodge, built as a farmhouse in the 1860s, has welcomed guests since the 1920s. The art gallery and gift shop features products by Northeast Kingdom painters, artists, writers, and craftspeople and the restaurant uses local farm-fresh produce.

Open daily June–March 7 am–10 pm.

802-533-2647 • 1608 Craftsbury Road, Greensboro, VT
www.highlandlodge.com

 studio workshop   craft marketplace   special attraction

The Craftsbury Inn

Bill and Kathy Maire welcome you to their 1850 country home, which has served as an inn for over 50 years. The inn has a fiber farm with sheep, cashmere, and angora goats and llamas. Handspun wool and knit and woven products are available.

Open daily. Closed first two weeks of November and all of April.

802-586-2848 · 107 South Craftsbury Road, Craftsbury, VT
www.craftsburyinn.com

David Brown Woodworking

Find furniture, woodenware, or even landing nets for fishing at this woodshop. Dave Brown turns local hardwoods on his lathe to create exquisite functional plates, platters, and bowls.

Open year-round by appointment.

802-586-9625 · 91 Young Road, Craftsbury Common, VT

From Craftsbury, turn right (east) on Creek Road. At first fork turn left on King Farm Road. At first intersection turn right on Young Road. First driveway on left.

Craftsman working in the David Brown Woodworking shop

Maple Leaf Llamas

On a hillside in this scenic village in Northern Vermont are 20 llamas watched over by Susan and Ned Houston. Whatever visitors do—steal a "kiss" from a friendly llama, take a walk with a llama, follow a farm tour, or purchase yarn and other products, or even a llama or two—they will most certainly

 lodging   restaurant   artist gallery

leave with lots of knowledge about these amazing animals.

Open year round, please call ahead.

802-586-2873 · 654 North Craftsbury Road, Craftsbury Common, VT

Mill Village Pottery

This working studio is located in a pristine, tranquil landscape with stunning mountain views. The gallery is full of unique

functional and one-of-a-kind Raku pieces. Potter Lynn Flory works in a variety of clays and glazes and will explain any aspect of her inspiration, design and materials.

Open daily May–March 10 am–5 pm.

**802-586-9971 · 6 Mill Village Road, Craftsbury Common, VT
lynnspottery@aol.com**

Continue North out of Craftsbury Common on the North Craftsbury Rd. Turn right onto Mill Village Pottery; studio immediately on the right.

Craftsbury Outdoor Center

The Center's campus encompasses over 140 acres of woodlands on the shores of Great Hosmer Lake and the trail network involves more than 70 landowners. In addition to

accommodations for groups, families, and individuals, the Center offers a variety of activities including world-class sculling and running camps, Elderhostel courses on Vermont ecology and culture, and cross-country skiing, mountain biking, hiking, and birding.

**802-586-7767
535 Lost Nation Road,
Craftsbury Common, VT**

Continue on Mill Village Rd. Follow signs to the Center.

 studio workshop

 craft marketplace

 special attraction

Bread and Puppet Museum

27 Housed in a classic New England dairy barn built in 1863, the Bread and Puppet Museum showcases the largest collection of oversized puppets in the world. Thousands of puppets, masks, and graphics of the Bread and Puppet Theater are gathered as a "Theatrum Mundi," a "unified yet diverse, single creation rather than a collection of separate objects." The museum store is stocked with handprinted banners, posters, postcards, and books. Don't miss the annual June celebration featuring fresh sourdough rye bread, music, and performances.

Open June–November. Donations appreciated.

802-525-3031 · 753 Heights Road, Rt. 122, Glover, VT

Writing the Forested Landscape

Playwright, screenplay writer and film director David Mamet, who lived in Cabot, Vermont, for nearly 40 years, wrote that he chose the region because "it is beautiful, and it is the perfect place for a writer to live." Writers of all genres have drawn inspiration or made their homes in the Northern Forest, and Vermont can boast of many. A sampling of those whose fiction, poetry, or essays draw from the unique landscape and personality of Vermont's Northeast Kingdom includes Wallace Stegner, Galway Kinnell, Grace Paley and Reeve Lindbergh. Some of their works are set in the Northern Forest, others not, but all draw from what Vermont author Howard Frank Mosher described in Stranger in the Kingdom *as "a good but eminently improvable place, where the past was still part of the present."*

 lodging   restaurant   artist gallery

Old Stone House Museum & Museum Shop

Spend some time on this complex of five historic 19th-century structures and 60 acres of field and pasture. The Museum exhibits a wide range of handmade objects dating from the late 18th through the early 20th century, including furniture, hand woven textiles, quilts, hooked and braided rugs, baskets, pottery, handmade tools, and folk art. The Shop features traditional handcrafts made by local artisans and specialty food products. Always something going on, the "Heritage Craft Workshops" in July, Old Stone House Day in August or the "Holiday Craft Workshops" in November are must dos.

Open May 15–October 15: Wednesday–Sunday 11 am–5 pm, October 16–May 14: call for hours. Museum Tours: $5 adults, $2 students.

802-754-2022 • 109 Old Stone House Road, Brownington, VT
www.oldstonehousemuseum.org

Continue North on Rt. 116. Turn right onto Rt. 58 East. In Orleans Village, look for signs to the museum. Turn left onto Tarbox Hill. At the stop sign, bear left onto Hinman Settler Rd. Turn right onto Old Stone House Rd.

EXCURSION TO DERBY AND NEWPORT

IMA Basket Shop

Irene Ames' brown ash baskets are made in the traditional style of the Sweetser family from the late 1800s to late 1950s. Three apprenticeships on Sweetser baskets have led her to her current collection of laundry and mid-sized baskets as well as various mini baskets patterned after full sized baskets.

Open year-round, please call ahead for hours.

802-895-4275 • 474 Gore Road North, Derby, VT
www.IMABASKET.com

Head West on Rt. 58 through Irasburg. Turn right onto Rt. 14 North. Continue on Rt. 5 North through Newport. Turn right onto Rt. 105 at the Derby Corner Mini-Mart, and after 0.5 miles, turn left onto Rt. 111. Continue 5.5 miles, and turn left onto Gore Rd.

 studio workshop

 craft marketplace

 special attraction

Traveling with Wildflowers & Hammond Wood Products

In her book, *Traveling with Wildflowers from Newfoundland to Alaska*, Phyllis Hammond's delicate illustrations portray the beauty and variety of native plants. This gray-shingled gallery showcases her varied work—ranging from realistic to non-objective—as watercolors, acrylics, prints, book, cards, and bookmarks. Milton Hammon's shingle mill and sugarhouse is up the road.

Open Saturday 10 am–5 pm, Sunday 1–5 pm,
or by appointment.

802-334-2685 • 3802 Lake Road, Newport Center, VT
hambo@sover.net

Stay on Rt. 5 South through the town of Newport, and turn right onto Lake Rd. just as you are leaving town, before Rt. 105 splits off of Rt. 5.

Kingdom Commons

This gift shop is located in the former "summer kitchen" of an 1865 farmhouse with a splendid post-and-beam barn and one of the few stand-alone milk houses left in the area. Limited editions of Northeast Kingdom treasures are on display including pewter beakers, wooden bowls, hand blown glass dishes, and original artwork.

Open May–December: Thursday–Sunday 12 noon–5 pm
or by appointment.

802-744-6600 • 52 Finnegan Road, Lowell, VT
trish@kingdomcommons.com

Shop is visible from Rt. 100, one mile south of Rt. 58, on the right.

Vermont Studio Center

Founded in 1984 to support the making of art as the "communication of spirit through form," this nonprofit, creative community serves 600 artists and writers from across the country and the world. The open, nurturing environment of the Center's award-winning 30-building campus in downtown Johnson is an attraction in itself. As the country's largest artist community, the 75 artists and writers participating each month in 4–12 week independent studio residencies are selected to represent an intentional mix of media, culture, experience, and ages. In addition, the Center provides the resource of 7 distinguished visiting artists and writers per month, presenting

lodging   restaurant   artist gallery

their work and being available for individual studio visits and writing conferences. The public is welcome to stroll the streets and visit the gallery, which features changing exhibits of visiting faculty and students.

Open year-round.

802-635-2727 • Johnson, VT • www.vermontstudiocenter.org

Butternut Mountain Farm

Got maple? There is no shortage of maple products in this old-fashioned store—syrup, sugar, and candy—in this crowded store filled with local delectables. You'll find everything you need to tap your own sugar maple.

Open daily Monday–Saturday 9 am–5:30 pm, Sunday 10 am–4 pm.

802-635-2329 • Main Street, Johnson, VT
sales@vermontmaplesugarcompany.com

Milk Room Gallery

Find what you're looking for in this cozy gallery. Watercolors, oils, acrylics, and pastels depict the Vermont landscape. Visitors will also find pottery and jewelry by local artisans.

Open Tuesday–Friday 10 am–5 pm, Saturday 10 am–3 pm.

802-644-5122 • 105 Main Street, Jeffersonville, VT
www.milkroomgallery.com

Studio Art Center

Founded in 1984 to support art making "as the communication of spirit through form," the Vermont Studio Center is a creative community serving artists and writers from around the world. As the nation's largest artists' community, each year the Center provides four- to twelve-week independent studio residencies to 600 international artists and writers selected to represent a mix of media, culture, experience, and ages. As an additional resource, each month distinguished artists and writers are invited to spend a working week at VSC presenting their own work and serving as mentors to residents interested in studio visits and writing conferences. The Center's campus in Johnson is an attraction in itself, and the public is welcome to stroll the streets and visit the gallery, which features the work of visiting faculty and students.

 studio workshop

 craft marketplace

 special attraction

Quilts by Elaine

Quilts are made using traditional designs and quilt maker Elaine van Dusen explains the history and many uses of her work. The shop is located in four rooms of her home, with each arranged differently with beds and quilts, items for children, wall hangings, couch throw pillows and her signature, "Vermont's Shin Warmers."

Open June–October Tuesday–Saturday 10 am–4 pm.

802-644-6635 or 866-644-6635 • 127 Main Street, Jeffersonville, VT • www.quiltsbyelaine.com

Cotswold Furniture Makers

This new retail space showcases Shaker-inspired, furniture designed by John Lomas and built by six skilled craftsmen. Furniture for the home and office uses at least 70% sustainably harvested lumber. "Our guiding principle is simple: The use of top quality hardwood lumber, modern tools and equipment, and traditional joinery techniques, guarantee the integrity of each piece for life."

802-253-3710 • 132 Mountain Road, Stowe, VT

Brass Lantern Inn Bed & Breakfast

In the heart of Stowe, visitors will be charmed during their stay in this restored 1810 carriage barn and house on the National Historic Register. Each room features antiques and period décor and quilts, photos, and crafts are by local artisans. A member of Vermont Fresh Network, a full breakfast features ingredients from local farms.

Open year-round; office 7 am–9 pm.

802-253-2229 • 717 Maple Street, Stowe, VT
www.brasslanterninn.com

Travel 0.5 miles north on Rt. 100 from Village Center (Stowe intersection of Rts. 100 & 108). Inn B&B is on left.

 lodging   restaurant   artist gallery

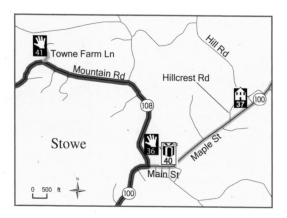

Haymaker Card & Gift

Orah Moore is a card maker and her hand-tipped photographic cards can be found at this fun and artful gift shop in the heart of historic downtown Morrisville, where service meets style! Local images also adorn recycled blank journals and framed photos. Look for locally made jewelry, origami, soap, and bath salts as well as many other handmade cards. The free artistic gift wrapping is a service that makes everyone smile!

Open Monday–Saturday 10 am–5 pm.

802-888-2309 · 84 Lower Main Street, Morrisville, VT
www.haymakerpress.com

10 miles north of Stowe on Rt. 100, first store on the left as you come onto Main Street in Morrisville (across from Thompson Bakery and the police station).

studio
workshop

craft
marketplace

special
attraction

Flying Colors

Practicing one of the oldest traditional arts, Brook Hemenway designs and weaves rugs, wall hangings or tapestries, pillow covers, chair cushions, table runners, and fashion bags. With designs ranging from Southwestern to contemporary, she uses vibrant colors and does everything by hand on her two 45″

Flying Colors fabric sample

walking looms and numerous work tables.

Open Monday 12 noon–5 pm, Wednesday 3–7 pm, or by chance or appointment.

802-888-2401 • 667 Washington Highway, 102 Union Street, Morrisville, VT

In Morrisville, turn right onto Congress St. then take the first left onto Union St. Studio is on the left across from Village Victorian Bed & Breakfast. Take door on far right and go upstairs. Return to Stowe via Rt. 100 south.

Vermont Furniture Works

Guided by a philosophy to create pieces of furniture that are visually and functionally appealing, this retail space showcases graceful traditional designs with an eye on fine craft and future use. The cabinetmaker and finisher sign each piece, reinforcing the notion of personal pride and creativity. The showroom displays reproduction "high country style" furniture that recalls its New England roots.

Open daily 9 am–6 pm.

802-253-5094 • 38 Main Street, Stowe, VT www.vtfurnitureworks.com

West Branch Gallery and Sculpture Park

The sculpture studio of Chris Curtis and the painting studio of Tari Swenson come together in this charming gallery and sculpture park. Enter the gallery to find calligraphic sumi ink on rice paper, oil landscapes, watercolors, and words. Wander through the sculpture garden and gaze on steel and contemporary stone-quarried granite and natural boulders, fountains, and

🏠 lodging   🍴 restaurant   📷 artist gallery

mobiles. You can also see the work of over 20 other local artists. Paths from the park lead to the West Branch River.

Open year-round daily 11am–6pm.

802-253-8943 • 17 Towne Farm Lane, Stowe, VT
www.westbranchgallery.com

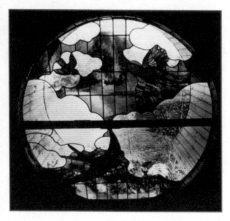

Stained Glass from Luminosity Studios

Luminosity Studios

Let there be Luminosity! This colorful workshop was born in 1975 in a former Victorian church. Barry Friedman creates custom stained and leaded glass architectural windows and fine period lighting for homes, businesses, and religious institutions nation wide.

Open year-round 10 am–5 pm or by appointment.

Closed Tuesday and Saturday.

802-496-2231 • 4276-4 Main Street, The Old Church,
Waitsfield, VT • www.luminositystudios.com

Artisans' Gallery

Infused with color and light, this renovated 100-year-old building is filled with delightful arts and crafts. Run by seven local artists as a cooperative, this gallery features the work of 115 artists from throughout the state, including artwork, jewelry, fiber, fine art, bowls, pottery, baskets, stained glass, furniture, and photography.

Open daily 10 am–5 pm.

802-496-6256 • 20 Bridge Street • Waitsfield, VT
www.vtartisansgallery.com

Turn left onto Bridge St. right in the village. Gallery is second building on the right.

 studio workshop

 craft marketplace

 special attraction

Chapter
7

Connecticut River Valley

The Connecticut River defines the long boundary between Vermont and New Hampshire, and its role in transporting goods and people has influenced the history and character of the communities along its shores and tributaries. Immerse yourself in the currents of local craft and artistic traditions on this two-day tour of its vast watershed.

Begin among the elegant estates of St. Johnsbury, Vermont, with a visit to the Northeast Kingdom Artisans Guild or the historic Fairbanks Museum and Planetarium with its impressive natural history collections. Don't fooled by first impressions as

Photos by: Jerry & Marcy Monkman/EcoPhotography.com

you head south through the hills of eastern Vermont. A dairy barn that no longer houses Jerseys or Holsteins might be a sculptor's workshop. A white steepled church could be an eclectic gallery or a gateway to walking trails and gardens.

Cross the Connecticut in Wells River and enter New Hampshire, where the motto "Live Free or Die" is reflected not only in the rugged granite landscape, but also in the work of local painters, weavers, and woodworkers. Follow the western slope of the White Mountains north to Littleton's dynamic Main Street, and explore Bethlehem's burgeoning craft community.

When you arrive in Lancaster, prepare to head up river into the Great North Woods and consider a side trip to the river's headwaters at the Connecticut Lakes. The rustic lodging and guided canoe trips that await your arrival are a fitting reward for those who follow the river to its source. After crossing the river back into Vermont, follow its tributary, the Nulhegan, to the village of Island Pond before turning south to round out the trip with stops in East Burke and Lyndonville.

Once an important transportation corridor for settlers coming north and logs heading south, let the Connecticut River transport you the hidden sites local creativity.

Cultural Heritage Profile

Legendary Log Drives

Massive log piles pouring into streams swollen by melting snow...

Men wading into icy shallows to push logs back out into the current...

Bateaux carrying food and supplies from camp to camp...

Dynamite blasting log jams from seething rapids....

These images describe some of the scenes common along the Connecticut River and other major Northern Forest waterways during the late 19th and early 20th centuries—the height of the legendary log drives.

Stretching from its headwater lakes near the Canadian border, down the full length of the boundary between Vermont and New Hampshire, and on through southern New England, the Connecticut served as a vital corridor for transporting logs downstream to the cities and mills where they were processed. From the long logs used to produce lumber, to the pulpwood that fed a growing paper industry, the river carried millions of board feet of timber from forest to mill.

Wearing spiked boots to grip the logs as they guided them downstream using peaveys and pike poles, river drivers were famous for their toughness in the face of long days and brutal cold. They also were known for risk-taking and courage when they needed to climb onto a tangled mass of logs to break a jam in the middle of a foaming rapid.

This quote from a 1960 interview with river driver Gerard Arsenault captures the spirit of the Northern Forest drives and the men who worked them.

"I've seen the time when I'd get the key log loosened, and then before I could get back to the shore it was either a matter of jumping a log and riding the river ahead of the drive, or being killed and letting the whole mass go over me.

"What'd ya do? Why, you'd just stand there on the tail of a log, the front end up in the air a foot or two, like the prow of a canoe, with the water white as froth, coming almost knee-deep on your legs, using your long pike pole for a balancer to help steer, and keeping ahead of the jumbled, tumbled rearing mass coming downstream right behind you hell bent for election.

"Pray? Wan't no time for such things."

Connecticut River Valley

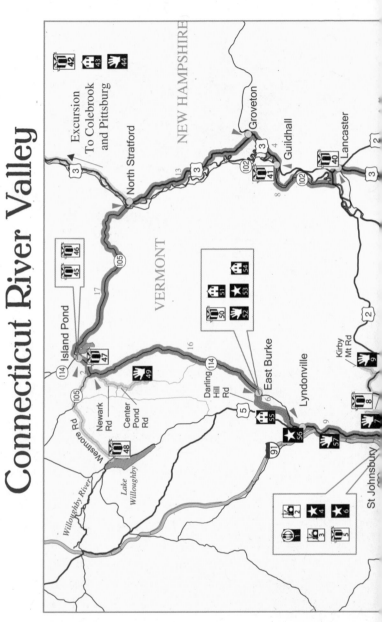

The main portion of the Connecticut River Va

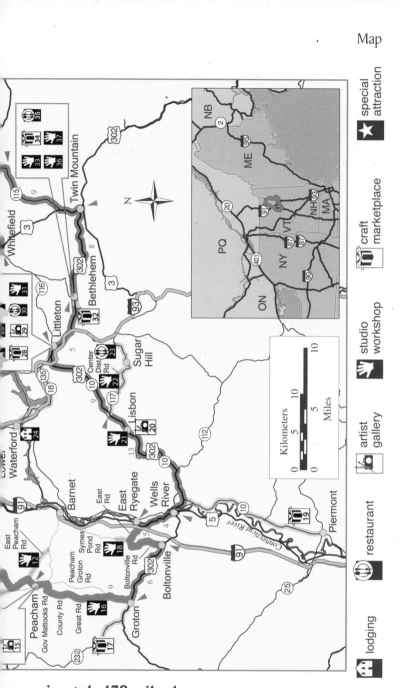

Map

special attraction ★

craft marketplace 🏺

studio workshop ✋

artist gallery 🎨

restaurant 🍴

lodging 🏠

approximately 178 miles long.

139

ST. JOHNSBURY

Elements Food and Spirit

Taste the countryside in this lovingly restored 150-year-old mill overlooking the Passumpsic River. Connected to the Vermont Fresh Network, this popular restaurant features ingredients, produce and artisan cheeses from Vermont farms and producers. Owner Keith Chamberlin takes pride in pointing out that, "everything we serve is made on site—pâtés, cured fish, and sourdough bread. Even the artwork is local."

Open 4 pm Tuesday–Saturday, open for dinner at 5 pm.
Open for lunch Memorial Day Columbus Day.

802-748-8400 · 98 Mill Street, St. Johnsbury, VT
www.elementsfood.com

Northeast Kingdom Artisans Guild

Find it all at this juried cooperative featuring works by more than 60 Vermont artisans, most of them from the Northeast Kingdom. With a focus on traditional crafts depicting Vermont landscapes, visitors will find forests, farmlands and gardens portrayed in braided wool, clay, ink, or paint. Other wonders on display include felted wool, hand-dyed yarn, forged iron, and blown glass.

Open Tuesday–Saturday 10:30 am–5:30 pm.
Call for extended holiday hours.

802-748-0158 · 430 Railroad Street,
St. Johnsbury, VT

Catamount Film and Arts Company

Cultivating the artistic voice of the Northeast Kingdom, two galleries at Catamount Arts feature paintings, photography, and mixed media work by local artists. The same building is home to a cinema where the best in American and foreign independent films are screened.

Open daily 1–6 pm.

802-748-2600 · 139 Eastern Avenue,
St. Johnsbury, VT
www.catamountarts.com

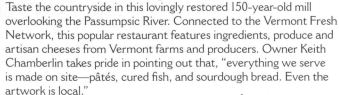

 lodging   restaurant   artist gallery

Mt. Washington Hotel

The Grand Scale of History

The Mount Washington Hotel was grand in scale from its very conception, even by the standards of nineteenth-century grand resorts. With a staff of 350 and a private telephone system and post office, it opened in 1902 as the most luxurious hotel of its day. Its magnificent red-roofed main building, designed to invoke the grandeur of an ocean liner, drew wealthy guests from Boston, New York and Philadelphia. The hotel's backdrop was even more impressive: New Hampshire's Presidential Range and the highest peak in the northeast, 6,288-foot Mount Washington.

Throughout its hundred-year history, the Mount Washington Hotel has hosted presidents, princes, and dignitaries from around the world. Its greatest claim to fame came in 1944 when it served as the site of the Bretton Woods International Monetary Conference, which resulted in the establishment of the World Bank and International Monetary Fund, and designated the United States dollar as the backbone of international exchange.

Known today as the Mount Washington Resort at Bretton Woods, this full-service destination features activities from golf to skiing at its location near Crawford Notch on Route 302.

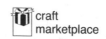 studio workshop

 craft marketplace

★ special attraction

Fairbanks Museum and Planetarium

Northern New England's premier museum of natural history
is a destination for every traveler. With a
mission to "foster a spirit of stewardship
and wonder toward our world" Museum
exhibits reflect the interdisciplinary and
eclectic nature of the collections. The
annual Fairbanks Festival Weekend in
September celebrates the culture and
artistic heritage of the region.

Open Tuesday–Sunday 9 am–5 pm.

802-748-2372
1203 Main Street, St. Johnsbury, VT

Fairbanks Museum

Classic Designs by Matthew Burak

A visit to this showroom uncovers an array of 18th century
American furniture and architecture. This business specializes
in making furniture parts and kits from solid wood in compelling
designs, such as Windsor, Queen Anne, Chippendale, and
Sheraton.

Open Monday–Friday 8 am–4:30 pm.

802-748-9378 · 84 Central Street, St. Johnsbury, VT
www.tablelegs.com

*From the Fairbanks Museum, turn right onto Central St., and take next
left onto Summer St.*

St. Johnsbury Athenaeum

A National Historic Landmark, the Athenaeum has served
as a center of culture and learning since 1871. The gracious
Victorian reading rooms with leather-bound books, elaborate
woodwork, and spiral staircases invite visitors to stay and
browse. The gallery is home to a permanent collection of more
than 100 19th-century paintings.

Open weekdays 10 am–5:30 pm.

802-748-8291 · 1171 Main Street, St. Johnsbury, VT

*Vermont's northeast corner was baptized the Northeast
Kingdom in 1949 by U.S. Senator George Aiken in remarks
praising its beauty.*

Tidbits

🏠 lodding 🍴 restaurant 📷 artist
gallery

Stephen Huneck Gallery

Dogs are always welcome! 400 acres of pasture with wildflowers and forest, walking trails, reflecting ponds, and sculpture gardens make idyllic surroundings for this gallery. Stephen Huneck features dogs in his playful prints, furniture, sculpture, and books and a chapel on site is open to all "breeds and creeds."

Open Monday–Saturday 10 am–5 pm and Sunday 11 am–4 pm.

802-748-2700 · 143 Parks Road, St. Johnsbury, VT
www.huneck.com

The Keeper on Horned Pout Pond

An 1800s homestead provides the quintessential backdrop for an eclectic mix of primitive, folk, rustic, and reproduction furnishings and crafts, including wrought iron pieces, tin ware, folk prints, candles, wreaths, garlands, pots, birdhouses, and other original work by area artists. Set amid 170 acres of rolling fields and woods and overlooking two ponds teaming with native "horned pout," the store provides a different approach to the traditional retail site.

Open May–December: Friday–Monday 10 am–5 pm or by appointment.

802-748-3417 · 1838 Spaulding Road, St Johnsbury, VT

D. M. Randall Furniture

David Randall makes furniture reproductions, restorations, and custom designs in wood. In his small shop, visitors can find oval Shaker boxes and highboys.

Open weekdays 9 am–3:30 pm or by appointment.

802-695-8178 · 1492 Kirby Mountain Road, Concord, VT

Emergo Farm B&B

Emergo Farm is a 6th-generation dairy farm. It was built by hand using traditional post and beam construction in 1890 and 1897 by the great-great-grandparents of the Webster family, who still live and work here. The adjacent three-story farmhouse and barn is located in a picturesque setting overlooking Danville village. Visitors can tour the historical and modern free stall parlor where the family milks 9 head of Holsteins. Visitors are also encouraged to help with farm

 studio workshop    craft marketplace   special attraction

chores, such as feeding calves or goats. Hike Webster Hill for a romantic picnic area with panoramic views.

Farm tours, May–October: Monday–Saturday 4–7 pm, or by appointment. $10 family of 4, $5 per adult.

Emergo Farm Bed and Breakfast

802-684-2215 • 888-383-1185
261 Webster Hill Road, Danville, VT • www.emergofarm.com

Take Rt. 2 west from St. Johnsbury. Turn right at the blinking light in Danville onto Diamond Hill Rd. Go 0.6 mile, turn right onto dirt road. Farm is second on the left.

Gallery at Still Run

11

This picturesque woodshop and gallery in the hills of Peacham specializes in painted pine country furniture by Paul G. Evans. Shaker boxes, beeswax candles, tin ware and other country items fill the retail space. Inspired by rural colonial New England, Paul builds using tools and techniques from many years ago. "Hand-planed boards and moldings, and the aged look of my painted finished add to the uniqueness of each piece."

Open seasonally; Memorial Day–Christmas weekends 10 am–5 pm or by appointment.

802-592-3219
107 Still Run, Peacham, VT
www.paintedpineman.com

Head South on Peacham Groton Rd. (Highway 1). Turn right onto Ewell Mill Rd. First right onto Still Run.

 lodging   restaurant   artist gallery

Magnus Wools

There is something happening in every season at this rural studio. In summertime, sheep fleeces are washed and fleece and wool yarns hand dyed. Hand spinning is done year-round from the weaver's sheep. Between September and April, area rugs, scarves, and hangings are made from start to finish, woven with hand-dyed wool yarn from a mill in Maine, from the hand-spun wool from the weaver's sheep, or from unspun inlaid wool from her flock.

Open year-round. Call for hours.

802-592-3320 · 2888 East Peacham Road, Peacham, VT
magnuswools@kingcon.com

Return to Peacham Groton Rd. (Highway 1). This becomes the Bailey-Hazen Rd. Turn left onto the Peacham Road, towards East Peacham. Continue straight through the intersection onto East Peacham Rd. (Highway 2).

Peacham Corner Art Guild

Right in the red building in the heart of Peacham Village, the Peacham Corner Art Guild offers handmade crafts alongside antiques. More than 20 artisans contribute one-of-a-kind pottery, paintings, photography, calligraphy, jewelry, woven baskets, aroma therapy products, candles, soaps, condiments, and preserves, knitted clothing and hand woven rugs to fill the shelves with vibrant color. Guild members, who are pleased to answer questions and point out particular treasures, staff the store.

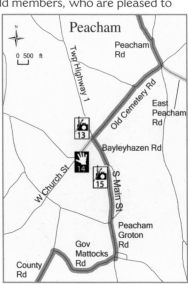

Open Monday–Saturday
10 am–5 pm,
Sunday 11 am–5 pm.

802-592-3332
583 Stanton Road, Danville,
643 Bailey-Hazen Road,
Peacham, VT
dodgedesigns@kingcon.com

Return to the intersection in East Peacham. Turn left onto Old Cemetery Rd.; follow to Peacham Village.

 studio workshop

 craft marketplace

 special attraction

How Sweet It Is!

Springtime "sugaring" is a North Country tradition as old as the hills. Indians taught early European settlers how to tap the abundant maple trees and boil the sap for syrup and sugar. Today, more maple syrup flows from Vermont than any other state in the nation.

Across the Northern Forest, the first warm days of spring signal the start of the hard but rewarding work of gathering

Sugaring in Greensboro, VT

and boiling sap gathered from trees in what locals call sugar bushes. It takes 40 gallons of sap to make one gallon of syrup, and each tapped tree provides about 10 gallons of sap per season. Sugarhouses in this guide offer a glimpse into the traditional process that ends when you top off your pancakes with the finest Grade A Northern Forest syrup.

Sugarshack in Greensboro, VT

 lodging restaurant artist gallery

Stitches by Julianna

Julie Kempton makes custom children's clothing and accessories out of whimsical cotton designs. Visitors will see her in production—cutting fabric, sewing, or applying finishing touches. Browse through the fabric inventory!

Open Tuesday and Thursday 10 am–12 noon or by appointment.

802-592-3005 • 1 Village Farm, 94 Church Street, Peacham, VT juliannak@charter.net

Parker House Gallery

This gallery in a 1830s Greek Revival building is in the heart of Peacham, a National Historic Village Center and the location of many period homes and architecture dating back to the Revolutionary War. The Gallery's collection includes original oil paintings by Rodney Reis and other artists, as well as select antiques.

Open daily 10 am–5 pm.

802-592-3079 • 511 Bailey Hazen Road, Peacham, VT www.parkerhouse.com

Parker House Gallery Painting

 studio workshop

 craft marketplace

 special attraction

Snowshoe Farm, LLC

16

Come visit a flock of friendly animals! Terry and Ron Miller raise breeding quality alpacas on this picturesque farm. They also process the fiber and spin, knit, and weave it into clothing and accessories or sell the fiber to hand spinners and yarn to knitters and crotchetier.

Open by chance or appointment.

802-592-3153 • 520 The Great Road, Peacham, VT
www.alpacas-snowshoefarm.com

Head South on Bailey-Hazen Rd. This becomes the Peacham Groton Rd. In the village of South Peacham, turn right onto Gov. Mattocks Rd. Go to end. Turn left onto County Rd. Bear left at the fork onto The Great Rd., follow approximately 2 miles.

Montague Custom Woodturning & Teaching

17

Robert Montague draws on 45 years of turning and teaching in sharing the skills and pleasures of woodturning with one or two students at a time. He makes specialty folk toys and one of a kind tops. Call for a demonstration or lesson on the fine touch of turning wood.

Open March–November, weekdays.

802-584-3486
304 State Forest Road
(Rt. 232), Groton, VT
www.yestermorrow.org

Continue South on the Great Rd. Turn right onto Minard Hill Rd. (Peacham Groton Rd.) toward Groton. Turn right onto Rt. 302, then right onto Rt. 232.

Wooden Top

 lodging restaurant artist gallery

Coach and Carriage

Return to an age of elegance. Brenda Bandy constructs 1/2 scale Victorian carriages using basswood, balsa wood, dowels, slats, sticks, leather, fabric, and hardware. All are original and no two are alike. "I love making these carriages as I think back

to those days and often wish I had lived in them. My carriages create a romantic feeling of olden times."

Open year-round. Call for appointment.

802-584-3575 · 182 Symes Pond Road, East Ryegate, VT
candc@sover.net

The Round Barn Shoppe

Homemade fudge and ice cream made a visit to this 16-sided round barn a treat! The work of over 300 crafters fill the

shelves with local flavor and colorful souvenirs.

Open June–December:
Thursday–Monday
9 am–5 pm,
January–June:
Friday–Saturday
9 am–5 pm.

603-272-9026
430 Rt. 10, Piermont, NH

 studio
workshop

 craft
marketplace

★ special
attraction

The ARTS Gallery

It is one-stop shopping at this North Country artisan cooperative that displays and sells fine art. Watercolors, pastel, oils, photography, sculpture, fine jewelry, baskets, hand poured soaps, lotions, candles, textile arts, and furniture showcase unique perspectives of inspiration.

Open Wednesday–Saturday.

603-838-2300 · 28 Main Street, Lisbon, NH
theartsgallery@msn.com

Scott Brumenschenkel Cabinetmaker

In this 1,400-square foot woodworking studio, Scott Brumenschenkel builds a variety of projects from custom furniture to small boats. "My studio is a personal space in which I design and craft my work. My work combines the ease of modern milling with the centuries old techniques of handwork." Stop by to see completed pieces in his portfolio or to view finished pieces on display.

Open year round, please call ahead for an appointment.

603-838-5300 · 41 Lincoln Avenue, Lisbon, NH
www.brumenschenkel.com

Turn left onto School St. in downtown Lisbon. Turn right onto Grafton. Bear right onto Lincoln Ave.

P.C. Anderson Handmade Furniture

Uncompromising workmanship in wood is the basis of this unique elegant hardwood furniture, with every piece individually made using traditional joinery and construction. Some selected pieces are on display in the showroom and a wide variety can be custom made from the portfolio.

Open April–December, daily 9 am–5 pm. Open January–March by appointment or chance.

603-823-5209 · 253 Center District Road, Sugar Hill, NH
www.andersonfurniture.com

🏠 lodging   🍽 restaurant   🖼 artist gallery

Polly's Pancake Parlor

Polly's Pancake Parlor lives up to its name with unbeatable breakfasts and brunch. The restaurant features pancakes and waffles made from stone ground flours. Diners will want to bring home homemade pancake mixes and fresh maple products.

Restaurant: May–October: 7 am–2 pm. Retail store: by chance or appointment.

603-823-5575 · 672 Route 117, Hildex Maple Sugar Farm, Sugar Hill, NH · info@pollyspancakeparlor.com

Rabbit Hill Inn

One of the oldest inns in the country, Rabbit Hill was established in 1795 as the Samuel Hodby's Tavern on the midway point of an 18th-century trade route. The tavern welcomed traders and loggers working on the Connecticut River half a mile away. Innkeepers Leslie and Brian Mulcahy have maintained a connection to this historic legacy and created an ambiance of elegance today. It is repeatedly named one of America's best and most romantic inns.

Open daily.

802-748-5168 · 48 Lower Waterford Road, Lower Waterford, VT · www.rabbithillinn.com

 studio workshop

 craft marketplace

 special attraction

Treehooks/Taylor Moore Studios

25

This studio offers a place to hang your hat . . . literally! Diane Taylor Moore crafts wooden wall hooks after originals found in a 100-year-old Northern Fishing Lodge. Made out of cedar and hemlock, they hold pots and pans, fly fishing rods, or towels. Also a painter with over 30 years experience, her mixed media paintings include

Tomato Painting

textiles, papers, beads, and oil paint, with her most recent works depicting wildlife and plants.

Open year-round.

603-444-2436 • 110 West Main Street (Rt. 18), Littleton, NH
taylormoore@adelphia.net

Pull into Taylor Dentist Office parking lot on the corner of West Main St. and Fairview. Studio is located behind the office.

Fish Painting

Littleton Area Chamber of Commerce Art Show

26

What could be better than spending the day at this colorful art show against the backdrop of the sparkling Ammonoosuc River and peak foliage in the mountains? Over 60 artists from all over New England come to display and sell their work, transforming Mill Street into a lively market.

Last Saturday in September.

603-444-6561 • 120 Main Street, Littleton, NH
www.littletonareachamber.com

 lodging restaurant artist gallery

Miller's Fare Cafe & Bakery

Known as "the best lunch in Littleton," this busy gourmet cafe and bakery features homemade soups, salads, sandwiches, and fabulous desserts! Take in the view of the new covered bridge and working waterwheel from the splendid riverside patio deck.

Open Columbus Day–May 31: Tuesday–Friday 8:30 am–2 pm, Saturday 9 am–3 pm. Closed Sunday and Monday. Summer open daily.

603-444-2146
16 Mill Street, Littleton, NH
millersfare@surfglobal.net

League of New Hampshire Craftsmen

Variety and imagination take hold here. The League of New Hampshire Craftsmen's new gallery is a showcase of fine crafts including ceramics, jewelry, blown glass, textiles, metals, wood, basketry, and prints made by artisans from all over the Granite State. Work ranges from traditional and functional to contemporary fine art. Once a month, a featured artist offers demonstrations.

Open Monday–Saturday 10 pm–6 pm, Sundays 10 am–5 pm.
603-444-1099 · 81 Main Street, Littleton, NH
www.nhcrafts.org

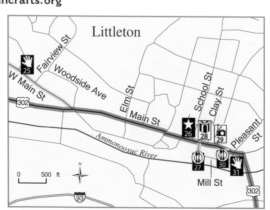

 studio workshop

 craft marketplace

 special attraction

153

Hermitage Art Gallery

This gallery offers an intimate space featuring eclectic images and styles that are frequently changing. All original artwork and limited edition photography is by well-known and newly discovered local artists. Take in a different featured exhibit every month or time your visit for the reception on the first Thursday evening of each month!

603-444-6114 • 71 Main Street, Littleton, NH
www.cavallinographic.com/hermitage

Floralatte

An original combination. Emily Herzig brings together all the senses in this sweet stop. The freshest flowers from all over the world, handmade fresh and dried flower arrangements and wreaths fill the room with color, while the coffee bar serves aromatic brews and fresh desserts. Local bands add music on summer weekend evenings.

Open Monday–Tuesday, Thursday–Sunday 10 am–6 pm.

603-444-7600 • 17 Main Street, Littleton, NH
www.FloraLatte.com

Contreras Gallery of Fine Art

Sal Contreras's original watercolors are mostly inspired by the surrounding landscape. Visitors will find over 500 pieces in his gallery or can watch him work in the connected studio. Call to arrange a demonstration or private group lesson!

Call for hours.

603-444-4414
9 Main Street,
Littleton, NH
www.contrerasart.com

lodging   restaurant   artist gallery

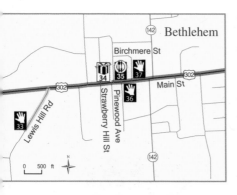

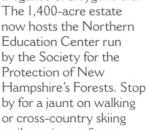

The Rocks Estate

Elegance of a bygone era. The 1,400-acre estate now hosts the Northern Education Center run by the Society for the Protection of New Hampshire's Forests. Stop by for a jaunt on walking or cross-country skiing trails or sign up for an education program. Also a Christmas tree farm, be sure to pick out the family tree or shop for holidays gifts from a collection of New Hampshire crafts.

Open year-round. Fees for some programs.

603-444-6228 · 4 Christmas Lane, Bethlehem, NH
www.therocks.org

Celebrating Traditional Crafts at the Fairbanks Museum

For more than 25 years, the Festival of Traditional Crafts at the Fairbanks Museum and Planetarium in St. Johnsbury, Vermont, has celebrated and helped preserve the skills, crafts, and folk traditions of eighteenth- and nineteenth-century rural northern New England. For two days each September, volunteer practitioners demonstrate and teach traditional skills using educational materials from the Museum's collections, as well as their own resources. Many demonstrators dress in period costumes and present skills and crafts ranging from shingle

making to splitting rails for fences to cider making, maple sugaring, spinning, weaving, dyeing, rug braiding, dowsing, candle dipping, and silversmithing.

The first day of the festival is enjoyed solely by the region's school children. The second day, always a Saturday, is for the general public. See the listing on page 142 to learn more.

 studio workshop

 craft marketplace

 special attraction

Whitefeather Studio

33 Sensitively rendered portraits in watercolor, pastel, and oil are on view in this studio. Artist Amy Delventhal captures local landscapes in realistic style. Pick up one of the few limited edition Giclee prints or peruse a small assortment of cards.

Open July–October.

603-869-3287 · 65 Lewis Hill, Bethlehem, NH
www.amywhitefeather.com

wrenOVATION!

34 Step into this marketplace of truly gifted artisans and discover a thoughtful gift or a treasure for yourself! Linger and be inspired by the unusual and unique work of over 100 artisans who make pottery, jewelry, woven rugs, baskets, candles, cards, and specialty foods. The store and gallery is owned and managed by The Women's Rural Entrepreneur Network, a nonprofit organization working to support market access to rural entrepreneurs, runs wrenOVATION.

Open daily 10 am–5 pm.
Call for winter hours.

603-869-3100
2013 Main Street,
Bethlehem, NH
www.theshopatwren.com

 lodging restaurant artist gallery

Reinvigorating Rural Life

The Women's Rural Entrepreneurial Network (WREN) brings people together to create and nurture meaningful relationships, sustainable livelihoods, and vibrant communities. Founded in 1994 as an organization to uplift women's lives and livelihoods, today WREN is among the fastest growing member-based organizations in New Hampshire, and its programs address the needs and aspirations of rural residents, business owners, and the town of Bethlehem.

As a women-led organization, community building is at the heart of WREN's work. With programs in entrepreneurial support, community and economic development, and technology and market access, the organization touches the lives of nearly 700 members—women, girls, and an increasing number of men.

To learn more about WREN and its members' businesses, stop by and pick up a complimentary copy of their quarterly publication, The WRENzine. *As part of its market development program, WREN's retail store, OVATION, features the work of more than 100 artisans from across northern New Hampshire and Vermont.*

See the listing on page 156 for more details.

WrenOVATION!'s store front

 studio workshop

 craft marketplace

 special attraction

Cold Mountain Café & Gallery

Some of the area's most interesting fare emanates from the kitchen of this quirky, 34-seat storefront. Chef-owners David Brown and Jack Foley will delight customers with baked salmon for dinner or interesting sandwiches for lunch, enjoyed in a room with pale yellow walls hung with changing local art, halogen lights, and votive candles on bare wood tables.

Lunch: Monday–Saturday 11 am–3:30 pm.
Dinner: Monday–Saturday 5:30–9 pm.

603-869-2500 • 2015 Main Street, Bethlehem, NH

Ron Smith Studio

You can't miss the whimsical genius behind the birdhouses in front of Ron Smith's home and studio. He also creates sculptural whirligigs with wood, paint, and found objects as well as builds sculptural furniture, architectural detail, and public art.

Open year-round by chance or appointment.

603-869-5427 • 2028 Main Street, Bethlehem, NH
ronsmithstudio@hotmail.com

Ragamuffins Design

Look for this light purple 1877 storefront in the center of town. Barbara Thompson creates stoneware pottery and porcelain ornaments using reflections of the world around her, particularly wildlife and landscape scenes.

Open year round, please call ahead for hours.

603-869-3387 • 2053 Main Street, Bethlehem, NH
btpottery@msn.com

  lodging   restaurant   artist gallery

Cherry Pond Designs

This small furniture factory employs local skilled woodworkers in the creation of solid cherry furniture in the shaker tradition of elegant simplicity. Visitors are invited to take a tour or browse finished pieces or factory seconds in the showroom.

Open Monday–Thursday 8 am–5 pm, Friday 8 am–12 noon, or by appointment.

603-586-7795 or 800-643-7384
716 Meadows Road (Rt. 115A),
Jefferson, NH
www.cherryponddesigns.com

Old Mill Studio

Nestled among the mountains, this gem of a gallery captures northern New Hampshire and Vermont ingenuity and inspiration. Its varied collection of original fine art and contemporary crafts, include paintings (oil, watercolor, and acrylic), photographs, linoprints, hand carving, pottery, hand-blown glass, jewelry (beads, silver, polymer, ceramic), textiles, mosaics, basketry, dried flower arrangements, iron works, hand turned bowls, wood crafted items, and sculpture.

Open Wednesday–Sunday 11 am–5 pm. Call for hours.

877-837-8778 · 36 King Square, Whitefield, NH
www.oldmillstudio.com

Fuller's Sugarhouse

Take a walk through this sweet-smelling sugarhouse. The lure of award-winning pure maple syrup, maple candy, pure maple cream, and dry sugar is hard to resist! Also tempting are locally made jams, jellies, pickles, and unique craft objects.

Open Monday–Saturday 9:30 am–5 pm, Sunday 10 am–3 pm.

603-788-2719 or 877-788-2719
267 Main Street, Lancaster, NH · www.fullerssugarhouse.com

 studio workshop

 craft marketplace

 special attraction

Guildhall Village General Store

41

Built in 1855 and listed in the National Register of Historic Places, the store still has its original shelves and cases. Come in for warm soup or a cold drink—the fresh cinnamon buns are a delight anytime! A wood-burning stove keeps the inside cozy in the fall and winter. Locally-made jams, jellies, honey, spices, bread, and pies are for sale.

Open Tuesday–Saturday 6:30 am–5 pm.

802-626-3713 · On the Town Green, Guildhall, VT

Creative Natives

42

A one-stop shop for beautiful handmade crafts: clothing, fine wool hats, kitchen items, hand-blown glass, furnishings, and wooden toys for all ages: fire trucks, trains, snowmobiles. Also delight in vintage linens, old glassware, aromatherapy, antiques, and pens and bottle stoppers created from moose antlers as well as portraits, photographs and paintings in oil and watercolors. All items are displayed in the homey setting of a building that housed Colebrook's first post office in 1800 and first hospital in 1930.

Open daily Spring–Fall. Winter: Tuesday–Saturday.

603-237-5541 · 117 Main Street, Colebrook, NH

The BALSAMS Grand Resort Hotel

43

For some 130 years, this grand hotel has welcomed guests from around the world to experience a stunning northern landscape and classic hospitality featuring private guest room accommodations, gold medal dining, and numerous facilities, activities and amenities of this 15,000 acre estate. An "Artist in Residence" program takes place during the summer and stimulating lectures, historic tours, and nature programs are offered in all seasons.

603-255-0600 · 800-255-0600 · Rt 26, Dixville Notch, NH
www.TheBALSAMS.com

Prospect Mountain Woodworkers

44

Local wildlife and scenic themes are captured in the scrolled or routed woodwork of Pete & Lainie Castine. They make breadboards, trivets, cabinet knobs, wall shelves and plaques, birdhouses and feeders, signs, and a variety of inventive and decorative woodcarvings. The view outside, a sweeping

160   lodging   restaurant   artist gallery

panorama of mountains and orchard, adds to the beauty of this visit.

Open April–October: Wednesday–Sunday 9 am–5 pm.

603-538-6777 · 266 Danforth Road, Pittsburg, NH
www.prospectmtnww.com

Travel North on Rt. 3. From the Pittsburg Town Line at the Green Metal Bridge, continue for 11.5 miles. Turn left onto Danforth Rd., across from Pittsburg Home Center. Continue to end. Look for the "Prospect Mountain Woodworkers" sign, and "Castine" mailbox. Turn left after the mailbox. Bear right at the fork. Continue to the top of the hill.

Simon the Tanner

This family outfitter carries local crafts—lampshades, soaps, candles, syrups, and walking sticks—in addition to a full line of shoes, boots, and outdoors clothing.

Open Monday–Thursday 9 am–5 pm, Friday 9 am–3 pm, Sunday 10 am–5 pm.

802-723-4452
Corner of Cross and Main Streets, Island Pond, VT

Rebecca's Room

This charming gift shop has something in every corner. Rebecca Lefebvre makes whimsical dolls, ladies' hats, vests, aprons, and potholders as well as candles, jewelry, wreaths, and floral arrangements. She paints Vermont scenes on slate, sleds and muskrat boards.

Open Wednesday–Sunday 10 am–4 pm.

802-723-6657
37 Fitzgerald Ave.,
Island Pond, VT

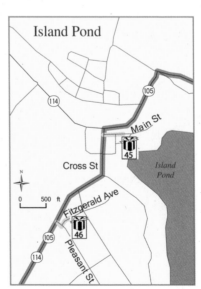

 studio workshop

 craft marketplace

 special attraction

Northern Wildlife

47

A source for all aspects of taxidermy—mammals, birds, fish—and to find handmade canoe paddles, snowshoes, and sap buckets. Look for wildlife paintings on moose antlers and a rotating exhibit of wildlife mounts native to the area.

Open Tuesday–Sunday 8 am–7 pm.

802-723-6659 • 550 Charleston Road, Island Pond, VT

Northern Exposure Country Store

48

A little bit of everything can be found tucked into the corners of this welcoming country building, which has been a store since the early 1900s. Local crafts are sold, as well as food, fishing supplies, and drinks.

Open weekdays 6 am–9 pm, Summer weekends 8 am–8 pm, Winter weekends 8 am–6 pm.

802-525-3789 • 1266 Route 5A, Westmore, VT

Wooley Buggah Farm

49

Anyone with an interest in knitting, weaving, or wool will enjoy a visit to this farm. Donna Coughlin keeps an open and inspiring bar, with natural colored and hand-dyed yarns, supplies, hats, and mittens. A look downstairs reveals the Nubian goats and Columbia ewes with their babies and Buttercup, a Haflinger horse. Across from the stall is a small dyeing kitchen.

Open weekends 10 am–4 pm or by appointment.

802-467-8600 • 182 Center Pond Road, Newark, VT

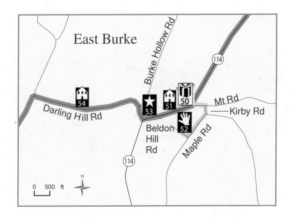

 lodging   restaurant   artist gallery

Bailey's & Burke

A local favorite. When you set foot in this 1800s old-time General Store, you'll find all you need—gifts, local crafts, prints, specialty foods, and a bakery offers tempting treats! Don't overlook the rows of glass candy jars filled to the brim with sweets!

Open daily Sunday–Thursday 8 am–7 pm,
Friday and Saturday 8 am–8 pm.

802-626-9250 • 466 Route 114, East Burke, VT

Village Inn of East Burke

Located in the heart of East Burke, this charming 1845 farm hosts comfortable lodging and dining, where guests are welcome to pick their dinner from the garden! Residents shop the farm stand for local honey, fresh produce, and home-canned goods. For the backwoods explorer, guide services cover fishing, wildlife photography, bird, fowl, and game hunting.

Open year round.

802-626-3161 • Route 114, East Burke, VT
www.villiageinnofeastburke.com

Clarner Woodworks

In a renovated 1850s barn, Doug Clarner produces fine, custom furniture from hardwoods like maple, cherry, and birch. Traditional joinery—mortise and tenon and dovetails—and a hand-rubbed oil finish characterize each piece. Visitors can see works in progress and purchase small items—mirrors, frames, and stools.

Open year-round by
appointment.

802-626-8935 • 170 Maple
Lane, East Burke, VT
www.clarnerwoodworks.com

 studio
workshop

 craft
marketplace

 special
attraction

Burke Fall Festival

Fun for everyone! This festival happens every year on the last Saturday in September with parades, a barbeque, live music, hay rides, games, and events. Local artisans and farmers can be found showcasing their wares!

802-626-4124 · Burke Village, East Burke, VT

Inn at Mountain View Farm

This famous Vermont stock farm is now an inn and restaurant, with a creamery, threshing barn, Morgan breeding barn, piggery, and icehouse. Be greeted along the way by donkeys, Belgian horses, Hereford, Holstein, and Black Angus cows. Experience old-fashioned America with a romantic horse-drawn wagon or sleigh ride amid the rolling hills and pasture's of the Inn's 440 acres. Savor farm-fresh Vermont foods while dining in the historic Creamery.

802-626-9924 · 3383 Darling Hill Road, East Burke, VT

The Wildflower Inn

On 570 acres at the crest of a ridge along Darling Hill, this Inn occupies a series of buildings—including a petting barn, coach house, old horse barn, and farm house—that make up this full-service country resort. Trails begin at the doorstep for hiking, mountain biking, and cross-country skiing. Fresh local produce is featured in the restaurant.

802-626-8310 · 2059 Darling Hill Road, Lyndonville, VT

 lodging   restaurant   artist gallery

Tidbits

For information about heritage and cultural events throughout New Hampshire's North Country, see the Arts Alliance of Northern New Hampshire's cultural calendar at www.aannh.org.

Burklyn Arts Council/Summer Craft Fair

Two chances to fawn over local treasures and meet local artisans and farm producers! The Summer Craft Fair and Christmas Market feature works by Vermont artisans, with proceeds supporting arts in local schools.

Fair: Saturday closest to the 4th of July, Lyndonville's historic Bandstand Park

Market: First weekend in December, Lyndon Town School

Calendar Brook Cabinetry

Using local northern hardwoods, the carpenters at Calendar Brook create custom-made furniture and cabinets, specializing in traditional and shaker designs.

Open weekdays 7 am–5:30 pm.

802-748-5658 • 4863 Memorial Drive (Rt. 5), St Johnsbury, VT

 studio workshop

 craft marketplace

 special attraction

Chapter
8

White Mountains

This two-day circuit traverses a region that has witnessed both the birth of modern paper industry and the creation of one of the first national forests in the eastern United States. Today the landscape of the White Mountain Tour provides inspiration for scores of fine artists and craftspeople who await your visit.

The journey starts in Bethel, Maine, where white clapboard homes, historic inns, and the Sunday River Ski Resort come together in a village with a 19th-century aesthetic and contemporary bustle. Semi-precious gems found in the surrounding mountains provide the raw material for local jewelers' creativity. Join the rock hounds in a local quarry, and you may find your own rough bit of amethyst or tourmaline.

Photos by: Jerry & Marcy Monkman/EcoPhotography.com

Follow the Androscoggin River upstream to Berlin, New Hampshire, to explore a reproduction 19th-century logging camp, complete with working blacksmith shop, at the Northern Forest Heritage Park. Heading south toward North Conway, you'll pass through the White Mountain National Forest, and the shadow of Mount Washington—the tallest mountain in the Northeast at 6,288 feet. Along the way you'll find some of the best hiking in New England, including access to a long section of the famed Appalachian Trail.

In North Conway take in the view of the Cathedral Ledges, and look among the retail outlet stores to find a wide range of handcrafted products. Conway serves as a gateway between the rocky peaks of the White Mountains and the rolling foothills of western Maine where orchards and agriculture begin to dominate the landscape. Round out this tour with visits to Norway and Paris, Maine, where you'll find a local art collective, a historic horticultural center, and the source of some of the finest balsam pillows in the world.

All along the way, be sure to stop and smell the balsam—as well as the pine, spruce and maple—of the White Mountain Tour.

Cultural Heritage Profile

Harvesting and Hospitality in the White Mountains

The coming of the railroads to the White Mountain region in the mid-19th century sparked two trends which combined to spur creation of the White Mountain National Forest—one of the first national forests in the eastern United States.

Though logging had taken place in the region for decades, the arrival of railroads—some of which reached deep into the wilderness—led to more aggressive harvesting to feed the sawmills that were popping up across the region. In New Hampshire alone, at one point, 17 logging railroads crisscrossed the state to service 832 sawmills.

Just as they made it easier to transport timber out of the mountains, the railroads also made it easier to transport people into the region for recreation and relaxation amidst the spectacular White Mountain scenery. Increased accessibility, combined with new wealth generated by the industrial revolution, led to a dramatic rise in tourism and the related development of resorts and grand hotels during the late 19th century. At the height of this era, between 1885 and 1910, the White Mountain region could accommodate more than 12,000 people in its 200 hotels, inns, and boarding houses. Major hotels, such as the Crawford House, Profile House, the Maplewood, and the Glen House, featured their own train stations or livery service and offered amenities and comforts ranging from gas lighting to lawn tennis, and fine dining to mountain guides.

Photo courtesy of Bethel Historical Society

The increase in tourism, combined with wildfires and flooding caused by aggressive timber harvesting along the region's valleys and mountain slopes, eventually led to the first significant land conservation in the White Mountains.

On March 1, 1911, President Taft signed the Weeks Act, which authorized the federal government to purchase mountain and forest lands and return them to the public domain. In 1914, the federal government bought the first parcels of the White Mountain National Forest. Among the earliest transactions was the purchase of 7,000 acres in Benton, New Hampshire, from Bertram Pike for just over $13 an acre. Today the WMNF includes almost 800,000 acres in New Hampshire and western Maine, and is one of the most visited forests in the country with over seven million visitors annually.

White Mountains

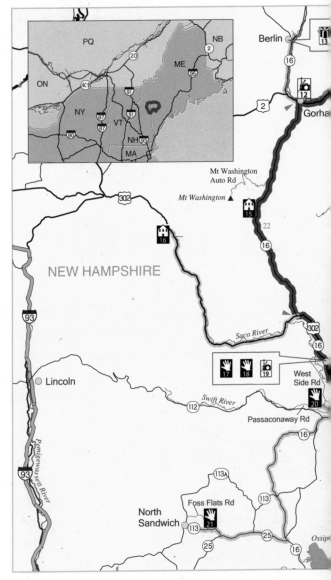

The main portion of the White Mountains lo

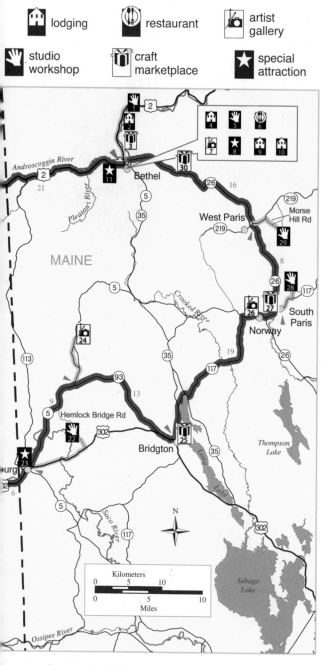

lodging **restaurant** **artist gallery** **studio workshop** **craft marketplace** **special attraction**

approximately 125 miles long.

BETHEL

 ### Tom White Studio at A Prodigal Inn & Gallery

Tom White's life-like bronze statues and oil paintings capture emotion, character, and features with life-like clarity. Find this gem next to the historic and elegant Prodigal Inn.

Open daily.
Partially Handicapped Accessible.
**800-320-9201 · 162 Mayville Road/
Route 2, Bethel, ME
www.tomwhitestudio.com**

 ### A Prodigal Inn & Gallery

This circa 1813 inn was completely renovated in 2003 to blend old-world charm and modern comfort. Guests can view original artwork throughout the inn or visit the adjacent gallery and work studio of bronze sculptor Tom White.

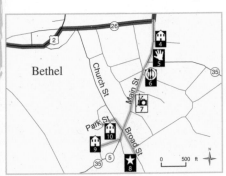

Open daily 8 am–8 pm.
Partially Handicapped Accessible.

**800-320-9201
162 Mayville Road,
Bethel, ME
www.prodigalinn.com**

 ### Timberlake's Home Store

Shaker furniture reproductions abound in the showroom of the Mayville House, a 19th-century farmhouse. In fact, most of the reproduction and custom furniture is made in the barn out back! Other handmade items—woodenware, cutting boards, and the signature "Perfect Spreader"—make unique gifts.

Open year-round.
**207-824-6545
158 Mayville Road (Route 2, east of Bethel), Bethel, ME
www.timberlakeandcompany.com**

 lodging   restaurant   artist gallery

Sudbury Inn & Restaurant and Suds Pub

The Sudbury Inn has operated since the turn of the 20th century. Current innkeepers Bill & Nancy Stowell White are

Maine natives and offer country inn-style lodging, fine and casual dining, and live entertainment for those visiting the Bethel area. View the paintings of local artists Barbara Traficonte and Thomas Higgins in the lobby.

Open daily.

800-395-7837
151 Main Street, Bethel, ME
www.sudburyinn.com

Bonnema Pottery

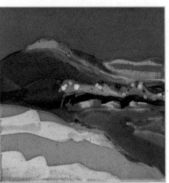

Inside this graceful Victorian barn, potters Melody and Garret Bonnema show their brightly colored stoneware and porcelain, lamps, large garden pieces such as birdbaths, and individual tiles in landscape designs. "We create our patterns by pouring glazes in overlapping layers, reflecting the depths of the landscape—including rich browns—and many shades of white, pink, yellow, and green. We use many blues, suggestive of sky, water, and distant mountains."

Open Thursday–Tuesday 9:30 am–5:30 pm.

207-824-2821 · 146 Main Street, Bethel, ME
bonnema@megalink.net

Tidbits

The summit of New Hampshire's Mount Washington is the site of the highest wind speed ever recorded—231 miles per hour in April 1934. The gust might have been even faster, but the wind gauge blew off the building, leaving room for speculation about the true ferocity of Mount Washington's winds.

 studio workshop

 craft marketplace

 special attraction

Cafe Dicocoa's Market & Bakery

6

Irresistible aromas greet you at the doorstep. Handmade breads and foods that use local products are featured in this restaurant and bakery. Cathi Dicocoa offers cooking classes and food demonstrations on health and sustainable farming. During the winter months, the focus is on global foods, highlighting the cultural and historic aspects of the world pantry.

Open Winter: 8 am–5 pm. Summer: 8 am–8 pm.
Closed March.

207-824-5282 · 119 Main Street, Bethel, ME
www.cafedicocoa.com

Mt. Mann Jewelers

7

All there is to know and see when it comes to Maine's mineral and gem history can be found here—a museum of Maine minerals, crystal cave for kids, and gallery with jewelry where gemstones mined by owner and artist Jim Mann emerge from rough material. Jewelry is handmade in an upstairs studio, using Maine Tourmaline, Amethyst, Aquamarine, and gemstones from worldwide locations. Mt. Mann produces custom gold and silver work along with brass, copper, and bronze. Look for extraordinary bookends and an unusual opal collection.

Open Tuesday–Friday 9 am–5 pm. Saturday 10 am–5 pm.
207-824-3030 · 57 Main Street, Bethel, ME
www.mtmann.com

In 1872, Scandinavians who came to work in the woods around Berlin, New Hampshire, started the Nansen Ski Club, which today is the oldest ski club in the country. In 1936, the club helped popularize Nordic ski jumping by building the largest ski jump in the East. The Nansen Ski Jump later served as the site of major competitions including Olympic tryouts.

Tidbits

  lodging   restaurant   artist gallery

Bethel Historical Society's Regional History Center

Founded in 1966, the Bethel Historical Society provides visitors with a doorway to northern New England's varied and colorful past. The Center operates from two adjoining properties listed in the National Register of Historic Places: the 1821 O'Neil Robinson House and the 1813 Dr. Moses Mason House. Collections document the history of northern New England, with a concentration on western Maine and the White Mountains. The Center offers more than a dozen

period rooms and exhibition galleries, craft demonstrations, research library operations, and museum shop sales.

Open Tuesday–Friday 10 am–12 noon, 1 pm–4 pm. Donations accepted.

207-824-2908 • 800-824-2910 • 10-14 Broad Street, Bethel, ME www.bethelhistorical.org

L'Auberge Country Inn & Bistro

L'Auberge is an intimate inn offering seven guestrooms with private baths in a renovated 1860s carriage house. The Bistro is a favorite for French-American cuisine served in relaxed, gracious elegance.

Open for dinner: Thursday–Monday; breakfast daily for Inn patrons.

207-824-2774 15 L'Auberge Lane, Bethel, ME www.laubergecountryinn.com

 studio workshop

 craft marketplace

 special attraction

Rivendell House

10

Long referred to as the Asa Knight House, the front portion of this residence was built in the early 1860s. Since then, it has evolved into a "big house, little house, back house, barn" configuration. Located in Kimball Park and on the National Register of Historic Places, the house has seen many uses over the years, but today is

a bed and breakfast focusing on Maine-grown, organic foods when available. The Inn's name is a symbol of the shelter and hospitality of J.R.R. Tolkein's Rivendell, where for guests it was "easy to stay long, and hard to leave."

Open year-round.

207-824-0508 • 16 Park Street, Bethel, ME
www.rivendellhouse.com

Songo Pond Gems

11

Rock hounds will enjoy collecting common and rare minerals! Several open quarries are cut into a granite ridge overlooking Songo Pond. Tours are available by appointment, so be sure to call ahead.

Open May–October. Call for appointment.

207-824-3898 • 66 Annis Road, Bethel, ME
ongo@megalink.net

Chapel Arts New England

12

The air is filled with arts inside this mid-1800s white-steepled church. Concerts span the ages from early music to contemporary jazz, and a gallery in the back displays photography and paintings by local artists.

Open June–October: Friday–Sunday 12 noon–6 pm.

603-466-2129 • 13 Glen Road (Route 16 South), Gorham, NH
www.chapelartsne.com

 lodging   restaurant   artist gallery

EXCURSION TO BERLIN

The Artisans Giftshop at the Northern Forest Heritage Park

Situated on the Androscoggin River, the Park tells the story of the region's rich woods heritage: the working landscape and the diversity of people and traditions. The collection in the Artisans Giftshop weaves this tale through baskets and braided rugs, woodcarvings and turnings, maple products, beeswax candles, honey, handmade soap, and handspun wool. The art gallery features a different artisan's work each month.

Open daily Memorial Day–Columbus Day: 12 noon–6 pm. Off-season: Monday–Friday 12 noon–5 pm.

603-752-7202 · 961 Main Street, Berlin, NH
www.northernforestheritage.org

Follow Rt. 2 east and Rt. 16 north to Berlin.

Sweet Memories

Each room in this Victorian town house is decorated in a different motif. Herbal wreaths, swags, dried floral arrangements, Victorian gifts, soaps, candles, essential oils, and potpourri are made with locally grown dried flowers and herbs.

Open February–December.

603-752-7081 · 45 High Street, Berlin, NH

Return to main loop through Gorham.

Pinkham Notch Visitor Center

Nestled at the base of Mount Washington in the White Mountains, the Center is run by the Appalachian Mountain Club and is the perfect place to begin or end a backcountry adventure. With miles of trails just outside the door—including the famous Tuckerman Ravine and nearby downhill and cross-country ski areas—these facilities can't be beat. Stay in Joe Dodge Lodge or warm up with hot soup in the cafe. The Trading Post features food, books, and gear from local businesses and information on local mountain lore.

Open year-round.

603-466-2725 · Route 16, Pinkham Notch, NH
www.outdoors.org

 studio workshop

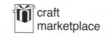 craft marketplace

 special attraction

177

Highland Center

This state-of-the-art center, run by the Appalachian Mountain Club, sits atop Crawford Notch, offering stunning vistas of the Presidential Range of the White Mountains. An environmentally innovative building, the Center offers overnight accommodations and outdoor recreation activities that celebrate the natural world. Guests can enjoy an all-inclusive dining and lodging experience, along with daily-guided outdoor trips and educational programs. In addition to browsing the Trading Post for food, books, and gear from local businesses, rotating art exhibits can be viewed at the historic railroad depot.

Open year-round.

603-466-2727 · Route 302, Twin Mountain, NH
www.outdoors.org

Essence-of-Art

This working art studio and interactive retail store provides support to crafters with developmental disabilities. Visitors can observe weavers at the looms and potters building handmade items. Visitors can find selections of finished pieces in the retail store, such as whimsical clay houses, bowls, vases, small clay animals, dishtowels, napkins scarves, and bags.

Open Monday–Saturday 9 am–5 pm.

603-356-9045 · 10 Seavey Street, North Conway, NH
tshedd@centerofhope.org

Earth & Fire Studio Gallery

See this harmonious fusion of hand-blown glass and ceramics. Glass artist Phil Michael Jacobs creates exquisite glass vessels using earth tones that reflect the beauty of the natural world. Ceramic artist Karissa Masse Jacobs creates stoneware pottery—mugs, platters, bowls, and jars—that is both visually artistic and highly functional. She is also known for figurative sculptures, "spirit vessels," expressing humanity's connection to the earth and the timeless cycles of life and death.

Open Sunday–Thursday 10 am–5 pm, Friday 10 am–6 pm, Saturday 10 am–7:30 pm.

603-356-8698 · 25 Seavey Street, North Conway, NH
www.earthandfirestudio.net

 lodging   restaurant   artist gallery

The White Mountain School of Art

In 1838, Benjamin Champney made a summer journey to North Conway, New Hampshire, that would change his life. He was so impressed by the mountain scenery that after several years in Europe he returned and bought a summer home. For the next 50 years he found fame and a good living painting picturesque views around North Conway.

Champney had plenty of company. Artists found the White Mountains irresistible—not just for their natural beauty, but also for the souvenir-hungry tourists. Among the 400 artists who worked in the region are many of 19th-century America's greatest landscapists: Albert Bierstadt, Thomas Cole, Asher Durand, John Frederick Kensett, Frederic Church, and Winslow Homer. The best White Mountain paintings are unforgettable monuments of American Romanticism, and even more modest works are often charmingly expressive of an era when many viewed nature as a source of divine experience. Today, we see the legacy of the White Mountain School of Art in the work of fine artists across the Northern Forest.

North Conway

League of New Hampshire Craftsmen

A spacious post and beam building with a perennial garden offers craft in all media made by members of this state wide

collective. Visitors can find products juried by a standards committee, including native hardwood chairs and tables, walking sticks, lamps, turned bowls, and botanical lampshades made with native flowers, grasses, and ferns.

Open daily 9:30 am–5:30 pm.

603-356-2441 · 2526 White Mountain Highway, North Conway, NH
leagueofnhcrafts@aol.com

 studio workshop

 craft marketplace

 special attraction

EXCURSION TO CONWAY

✋ Triquetra Leather Creations
20 A unique alchemy of artistically cut rare stones (predominately picture jaspers), sculpted leather and various hardwoods

creates one-of-a-kind boxes, vessels, and wall art. Through the execution of many primitive and contemporary techniques, Todd Barber creates ornamental objects pleasing to the eye. For the bird enthusiast, there is a fine line of jewelry depicting feathers of certain species.

Open Monday–Friday 10 am–6 pm.
603-447-5707 · 1424 Passaconaway Road, Conway, NH

From Rts. 16/302 in Fryeburg: head South on Rt. 16 to Conway. Opposite the junction with Rt. 153, turn right onto Washington St. Bear left onto West Side Road. Turn left onto Passaconaway Road. Triquetra is about 1.8 miles down on the right.

✋ Botanical Lampshades
21 Jennifer Allen is a 4th-generation botanical lampshade maker who welcomes visitors to her workshop. Stop in and watch the process as dried and pressed flowers, leaves, grasses, and ferns are layered between fiberglass and a clear top and the shades are laced together. When illuminated, the vibrant colors of the flowers bring the beauty of the outdoors inside. In the summer, visitors can explore the gardens where Jennifer grows her botanicals. Inquire about classes!

603-284-7468 · 95 Foss Flats Road, North Sandwich, NH
www.botanicallampshades.com

✋ Ooomingmak Foundry & Glass Studio
22 Stop by this gallery and studio to see glass ornaments and bronze sculptures made by Lee Ring using traditional methods of blowing into molds. Check the website for a schedule of demonstrations.

Open August–December.

207-935-3601 · 202 Hemlock Bridge Road, Fryeburg, ME
www.ooomingmak.com

 lodging   restaurant   artist gallery

Maine's Most Beautiful Mountain Village

Situated on a bend in the Androscoggin River and surrounded by some of Maine's most rugged mountains, Bethel was founded in 1774 as Sudbury, Canada, on the site of a once prosperous Abenaki community. European settlement grew after the Revolutionary War, and in 1796 the town was incorporated and given the name Bethel, meaning "House of God." While early inhabitants lived as farmers and woods workers, the arrival of the Atlantic & St. Lawrence railroad in 1851 brought new opportunities in manufacturing and tourism. Large summer hotels sprang up at Bethel Hill village, and the town became a way station for tourists visiting the White Mountains and Rangeley Lakes. Today, Bethel is a four-season destination for guided fishing trips, golf, hiking, shopping, fine dining, and some of the best skiing in the east.

Fryeburg Fair

Since its humble beginnings in 1851, the Fryeburg Fair, held by the West Oxford Agricultural Society/Fryeburg Fair Association, has grown to become Maine's largest agricultural fair. It is complete with six days of harness racing, a farm museum second to none, the world's largest steer and oxen show, and displays of early farm equipment. The Craft Center allows fairgoers to purchase handmade products directly from juried craftsmen. Each year, the Farm Museum offers daily trade and craft demonstrations, such as blacksmithing, cider pressing, maple syrup production, chair making, rug-hooking, spinning, barn loom weaving, apple dolls, dried flower wreaths, basketry, and wood-stove cookery.

Annually the first week in October.

207-935-3268 • Fryeburg, ME • www.fryeburgfair.com

 studio workshop

 craft marketplace

 special attraction

181

Harvest Gold Gallery

Harvest Gold Jewelry is a family-owned and operated company celebrating its 19th year in the North Country. The gallery's picturesque setting overlooks the White Mountains, Kezar Lake, and flower and sculpture gardens. Inside, visitors will find fabricated gold jewelry made using the ancient techniques of hand raising and forming, and featuring Maine gemstones. A selection of fine American art, glass, sculpture, and home accents compliments the jewelry. "Our theme is natural—we like fish, flowers, and butterflies."

Open year-round by appointment.
Open July–August, call for regular hours.

207-925-6502 • 88 Maine Street/Route 5, Center Lovell, ME
www.HarvestGoldGallery.com

Down Home & Company

Visitors will find a little bit of everything in this knitting, spinning, and consignment shop—hand spun and commercial yarns, spinning wheels, fibers, dyes, knitting supplies, and books. Handmade items by the Down Home Spinners include hats, shawls, scarves, tatted earrings, and ornaments. Look for gift ideas in wooden wine bottle stoppers, pens, quilted or

handwoven items, tole painted objects, and a self-published child's Easter story written by a Bridgton resident!

Open Sunday 12 noon–4 pm, Monday, Thursday–Saturday 10 am–5 pm.

207-647-8118
150 Main Street,
Bridgton, ME
braelynfarms@hotmail.com

lodging   restaurant   artist gallery

Commons Art Collective

A sunlit 19th-century storefront on pedestrian-friendly Main Street is home to this gallery of art that transcends the commonplace. An eclectic group of Maine artists represent diverse media— paint, sculpture, and textiles—to create beautiful, conceptual and distinctly original works of art. Exhibits rotate monthly.

Open year-round.

207-743-9808 · 447 Main Street, Norway, ME · artscoop@fareshare.com

The McLaughlin Foundation Garden & Horticultural Center

This historic 19th-century barn and house and 20th-century garden is on the National Register of Historic Places. The gift shop sells garden-related tools, books, and gifts including Maine-made soaps, jewelry, cards and condiments, and the lunchroom supports local growers, serving soups, salads, sandwiches, and desserts. Be sure to stroll through the two-acre garden's significant collections of wildflowers, hostas, irises, day lilies, and Maine's largest collection of lilacs. Don't miss the wildflower sale on Mothers' Day and the lilac festival and plant sale on Memorial Day weekend!

Open May–October. Donations appreciated.

207-743-8820
97 Main Street (Route 26), South Paris, ME
www.mclaughlingarden.org

 studio workshop

 craft marketplace

 special attraction

Forest Heritage and the Brown Company

While papermaking originated in Asia nearly 3,000 years ago, it was here in the Northern Forest that it was transformed into today's modern industrial process.

Among the earliest pioneers in this evolution was the Brown Company of Berlin, New Hampshire. The company entered the paper business 1881 using a new sulphite pulping process that used spruce, rather than the more expensive poplar required by many other companies. With the Brown Company's leadership, by the first decade of the 20th century Berlin claimed the largest newsprint plant in the world, with customers including the Boston Globe, *the* New York Tribune *and the* New York News.

Today, the former Brown Company headquarters is home to the Northern Forest Heritage Park, a logging history museum and visitor center that hosts educational events and celebrations at a reproduction turn-of-the-century logging camp on the banks of the Androscoggin River. Its Artisans Gift Shop features a range of authentic traditional crafts by residents of New Hampshire's North Country. See the listing on page 177 for more details.

Christian Ridge Pottery

A visit to this studio will take you through sprawling apple orchards with a magnificent view of the White Mountains. You'll also meet Scott Currie, Christian Ridge's Master Craftsman since 1987, whose 30 years of potting experience is reflected in his unique work. Call to arrange a guided pottery tour.

Open Monday–Saturday 10 am–4 pm.

207-743-8419 • 210 Stock Farm Road, South Paris, ME
www.applebaker.com

 lodging restaurant artist gallery

Maine Balsam Fir Products

This award-winning business situated on 111 acres of rural countryside and a lovely mountain brook hand-produces the finest balsam pillows in the world. Wendy and Jack Newmeyer started in 1977 by using leftover branches of local balsam fir trees cut for other wood products. Now with a team of neighborhood employees, they make 100,000 items a year for gift shops across the country and beyond. Creations vary from tiny sachets to large decorative pillows, draft stoppers, and trivets.

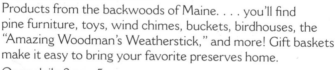

Open Monday–Saturday 9 am–5 pm.

800-522-5726 · 16 Morse Hill Road, West Paris, ME
www.mainebalsam.com

Maine Line Products

Products from the backwoods of Maine. . . . you'll find pine furniture, toys, wind chimes, buckets, birdhouses, the "Amazing Woodman's Weatherstick," and more! Gift baskets make it easy to bring your favorite preserves home.

Open daily 9 am–5 pm.

207-875-2522 · 297 Main Street, Greenwood, ME
www.mainelineproducts.com

 studio workshop

 craft marketplace

 special attraction

185

Chapter

Maine Mountain Heritage: The Western Mountains & Highlands Tours

The culture and heritage of the Maine Mountains reflect a people who have learned to make comfortable lives and masterful crafts in the heart of some of the most rugged forests in the eastern United States. From the state's tallest mountains to its largest lakes, everything about the Maine Mountain Heritage Tour is big—so big that this chapter is split into two journeys—separated by the mighty Kennebec River.

The Western Mountains Tour starts in Farmington, a college town where you'll find everything from cozy ear muffs to hand-dipped chocolates and one of the finest collections of handcrafted wooden furniture and accessories anywhere in the region. Heading north and west from Farmington, you'll wind your way into the mountains through ski country with stops ranging from a Native American museum and gift shop to a fine art gallery to a woodworkers studio before reaching the classic resort community of Rangeley.

With its wonderful logging museum and a variety of shops, restaurants, and inns, Rangeley marks a turning point where you begin the trip back over the height of land, along the Swift River to the Androscoggin and a return to Farmington.

The Highlands Tour is anchored by the community of Dover-Foxcroft, home of Moosehead Furniture and the 80-plus-member Maine Highlands Guild, and extends in two directions.

Start by heading west, traveling through a string of small towns on your way to Greenville. Stop at a blacksmith's shop, a buffalo farm, and a range of other shops before ending on the shore of Moosehead Lake. In addition to touring the local craft shops and studios, consider a trip on the restored steamboat Katahdin to learn about the natural and human history of Maine's largest lake.

Return to Dover-Foxcroft and then head east and north toward Millinocket. You'll find makers of traditional wood-canvas canoes, as well as shops featuring hand-blown glass and deerskin handbags, before reaching Millinocket and the gateway to one of the true gems of the Maine woods: Baxter State Park.

Adventurous travelers can consider an alternative route from Greenville to Millinocket via the legendary "Golden Road"—a remote logging road across private lands. Ask the locals for directions. Make sure you have a good spare tire, and remember that logging trucks have the right of way.

From the slopes of Maine's tallest peaks to the shores of its famous lakes, lose yourself in the forests, the art and the traditions of the Maine Mountain Heritage Tour.

Photo by: Jerry & Marcy Monkman/EcoPhotography.com

Cultural Heritage Profile

A River of People

Like other Northern Forest rivers, the Kennebec has long been a vital transportation corridor through a remote and mountainous landscape. Because of its strategic connection to other transportation routes in neighboring Quebec, the Kennebec has played a particularly notable role in American history.

Long before the arrival of Europeans, the route between the Kennebec River watershed and the Chaudiere River in Canada provided an important link for native peoples living along the Maine coast and the St. Lawrence River valley to the north—connecting people for trade, communication, and warfare.

Prior to committing his infamous acts of treason during the American Revolution, General Benedict Arnold led 1,100 colonial troops on a fateful journey up the Kennebec to launch a surprise attack on the English garrison at Quebec City. Along the way, the army lost more than half its troops to disease, desertion, and retreat in the face difficult terrain, rough waters, and the cold and snow of late autumn in Maine. The English soundly defeated Arnold's troops, but the story of their trip was immortalized in Kenneth Roberts' historical novel *Arundel*.

In the early 1800s, farmers and merchants improved the trails and portage paths between the Kennebec and Chaudiere rivers to smooth the way for trade with Canadian markets—creating what came to be known as the Kennebec Road, or Old Canada Road. Later in the century, hundred of thousands of Irish and

French-Canadians followed the route south to find work on farms, in the woods, and in New England's growing textile and shoe factories, bringing with them the religious, artistic, and craft traditions of their homelands.

Today, this vital historical travel corridor is celebrated through the efforts of the Old Canada Road Scenic Byway which runs from Solon, Maine, north to the Canadian border, and the Kennebec Chaudiere International Corridor—a cultural trail following the entire route between Quebec city and the Maine coast. To learn more visit www.kennebec-chaudiere.com.

Photo by: Jerry & Marcy Monkman/EcoPhotography.com

Maine Mountain Heritage:
The Western Mountains

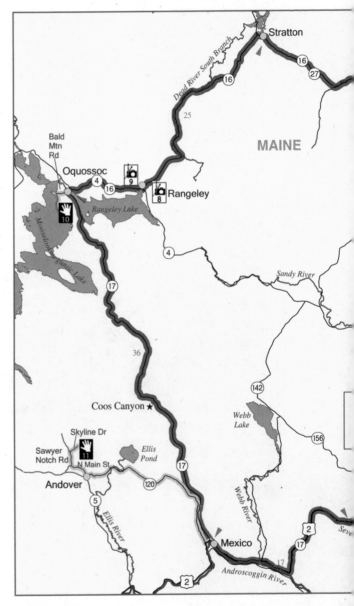

The main portion of the Maine Mountain Heritage: Th

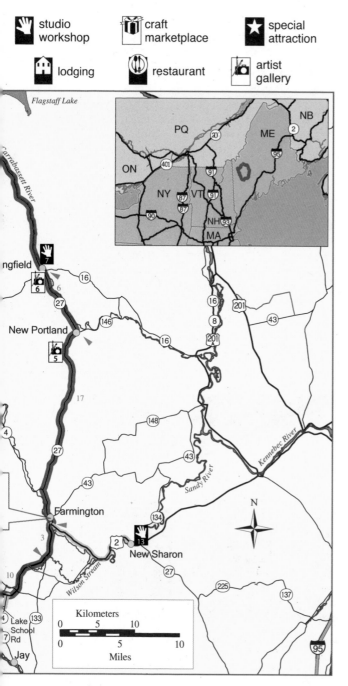

studio workshop
craft marketplace
special attraction
lodging
restaurant
artist gallery

Flagstaff Lake

ngfield

New Portland

Farmington

New Sharon

Jay

Kilometers
0 5 10

0 5 10
Miles

'estern Mountains loop is approximately 125 miles.

WESTERN MOUNTAINS

Mountain View Chocolate Shoppe
The aroma of chocolate beckons from the kitchen! This shop is the premiere chocolate lover's destination in Maine's western mountains, where luscious and tantalizing hand-dipped chocolates are created with only the freshest of ingredients.

Open year-round.

207-778-2500 · 248 Wilton Road, Farmington, ME
awesty@tds.net

Minikins
Keep warm through North Country winters. Susan Terese and the staff make clothing from Polarfleece, a Malden Mills fabric. Original designs for clothing and accessories are the source for many innovative and fashionable products. "We have brought back the traditional concepts of items like ponchos, earmuffs, and balaclavas for both children and adults."

Open Monday–Saturday 10 am–5 pm.

207-778-0500 · 157 Main Street, Farmington, ME
www.minikins.com

Minikins, storefront exterior

 lodging   restaurant   artist gallery

Maine WoodNet – Certified Creativity

Since 1999, Maine WoodNet has demonstrated that quality wood products and sustainable forest management go hand-in-hand in the Northern Forest.

Founded as a project of the Wilderness Society, Maine WoodNet is a marketing and manufacturing network comprised of more than 70 wood products businesses in Maine's Western Mountains. Members collaborate to strengthen business practices and increase their abilities to make and market their wood products. In 2002, Maine WoodNet became the first wood products cooperative in the United States to receive group chain-of-custody certification by the Forest Stewardship Council—officially demonstrating its members' adherence to the highest standards of ecological, cultural, and community sustainability.

By connecting fine craftsmanship with good forestry, Maine Woodnet helps furniture makers and other small-scale forest product businesses compete and thrive in an increasingly global market. Visit SugarWood Gallery in Farmington to learn more and to purchase fine products by Maine WoodNet members. See the listing on page 194 for details.

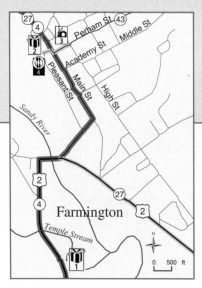

 studio workshop

 craft marketplace

★ special attraction

SugarWood Gallery

This charming gallery hosts the largest collection of locally-made furniture, home furnishings, accessories, and giftware in western Maine. Eleven artisans own and operate the gallery and 40 others display work. Visitors are treated to just about everything imaginable and unimaginable: live-edge frames and furniture; tables made from 150-year-old architecturally-salvaged material; hand-painted and pierced lampshades on turned bases; hand carved and painted signs; stunning stained glass pieces; maple syrup from a 200-year-old family run business; shaker style pine furniture and wood turned bowls and vessels; children's rocker and doll furniture; and balsam fir pillows.

Open year-round.

207-778-9105 • 248 Broadway, Farmington, ME
www.mainewoodnet.org

Knotty bench

The Granary Brew Pub & Restaurant

For a taste of the countryside, the Granary's handcrafted Narrow Gauge ale hits the spot. This full-service restaurant offers lunch, pub, and dinner menus featuring fresh Maine Lobster, seafood, steak, ribs, burgers, pasta, pizza, chicken, and vegetarian dishes, plus a children's menu.

Open daily 11 am–12 am.

207-779-0710 • 147 Pleasant Street, Farmington, ME
www.thegranarybrewpub.com

 lodging   restaurant   artist gallery

Nowetah's American Indian Store & Museum

Travel back in time through a truly outstanding collection of American Indian artifacts from the United States, Canada, and South America with a special focus on Maine's Abenaki. The museum has over 400 early Maine Indian baskets, porcupine quill boxes, birch bark containers, moose calls, moose hair work, and a 10-foot hunger canoe. There are also Maine nature items on display, including one wall with hides and furs that Maine Indians used for clothing and food. Visitors can also see a variety of early American Maine household antiques—butter churns, yarn winders, pewter candle molds, and spinning wheels. Take home a reminder of the visit with one of the genuine Indian crafts or fine art made by Nowetah Wirick and her daughter, Wahleyah.

Open daily 10 am–5 pm. Free admission.

**207-628-4982 • Colegrove Road,
Route 27, New Portland, ME**
www.mainemuseums.org

Woven rug

Stadler Gallery

Ulrike Stadler displays and sells contemporary paintings and drawings, sculpture, paper works, and tapestries by Maine artists. Visitors to this gallery can find her original artwork, including oil paintings and stained glass windows.

Open daily May–October 12 noon–4 pm.

207-265-5025 • 225 Main Street, Kingfield, ME
www.ulrikestadlerkozak.com

studio
workshop

craft
marketplace

special
attraction

195

Works in Wood

7

Shades of the forest for the table. These beautiful turned and segmented bowls come in a variety of shapes and sizes and are mostly made of hardwoods including Maine cherry, Maine maple, oak, walnut, rosewood and small pieces of ebony.

Open daily by appointment.

207-265-5622 • 1 Narrow Gauge Street, Kingfield, ME
ajeeray@tdstelme.net

Narrow Gauge St. is on the left, off Rt. 27, just past downtown Kingfield.

Rangeley Lakes Region Logging Museum

8

This Museum preserves and celebrates the heritage of logging in the western mountains of Maine. Its permanent collections include the memory paintings of camp clerk Alden Grant on logging in Kennebago in the late 1920s; the traditional wood carvings of local woodsmen such as the Richard family; 1912 to 1940 photographs and oral history of logging operations around the Richardson Lake area; Dr. Donald Bowen's journal of doctoring in the Brown Company's Magalloway camps in the early 1940s; knitting in the lumber camps; the Working the Woods exhibit on people of the Maine forest; and an ever-increasing collection of woods equipment such as Elijah "Tiger" White's forerunner of the skidder, John C. Tyler's half-size model wagon sled, and donkey engines, snubbing machines, pulp conveyors, and over 70 early chainsaws. The annual Logging Festival is a must-see! Publications include *Logging in the Maine Woods: The Paintings of Alden Grant*, edited by Margaret Yocom and Stephen Richard.

Open June–August: festival, last full weekend in July. Donations appreciated.

207-864-5595 or 207-864-3939 • Route 16, Rangeley, ME
www.mason.gmu.edu/~myocom/logging_museum

The last log drive in the United States took place on the Kennebec River in 1976.

Tidbits

 lodging   restaurant   artist gallery

Canoe Craft

Whether it's leaning against the shed out back, tied to the car roof, or floating along the edge of a lake or river, few things are more ubiquitous in the Northern Forest than canoes. And of all the styles you might see, none is more highly revered than the classic wood-canvas canoes produced by local craftsmen.

Modeled after its birch bark-covered predecessor, the hull of a wood-canvas canoe is built of light, resilient cedar shaped over a solid form. A single layer of canvas is stretched around the sanded and oiled hull and fastened with overlapping seams at the stems. By not bonding the canvas to the wood, the craftsman preserves the resilience and flexibility of the wooden hull. Spruce and ash are favored gunwale and trim materials.

Capable of carrying heavy loads in shallow water, and handling river rapids and wind-swept lakes, the wood-canvas canoe represents a fine expression of practicality, beauty, and grace.

Birds of a-Feather Gallery

Stop in to meet members of this involved group of fine artists who have formed a cooperative gallery housed within a bookstore. Their work includes watercolors, collage, prints, cards, fiber art, jewelry, painted furniture, lamps, photographs . . . many of the images are of the Rangeley region lakes and mountains.

Open daily 10 am–5 pm, Sunday 10 am–3 pm. Closed Tuesday.
207-864-2078 • Main Street, Rangeley, ME

Field and Forest Pressed Floral Art

Joe and Sally W. May carry on a tradition that can be traced to the storing of flowers and seeds in the family Bible by settlers embarking on a new life in a foreign region or country. Their pressed flower designs are a specialty. "My pleasure is to grow a variety of plants that differ in foliage, structure, color, size,

 studio workshop  craft marketplace   special attraction 197

blossom complexity, and thickness. The next step is to press the parts that I plan to use: leaves, stem, blossom or part of the root. . . . Then the enjoyment! Making a picture of pressed blooms: cards, mats, compositions."

Open year-round, call ahead.

207-671-6199 • 687 Bald Mountain Road, Oquossoc, ME

Pressed Flowers

Brenda Moore Stickney, Wildlife Artist

Working out of a solar-powered log home in the mountains of Andover, Brenda Stickney creates acrylic paintings and burnings of northern wildlife onto shelf mushrooms and shed antlers. Visitors to her gallery, Moose Mountain Trading Post, can find unique birch bark twig signs and pine air pillows, as well as enjoy the spectacular setting.

Call ahead.

207- 357-7004 • 188 Skyline Drive, Andover, ME
www.brendamoorestickney.com

Turn right on North Maine St. at the junction of Rt. 120 and Rt. 5. In two miles turn right on Sawyer Notch Rd. for one mile, then turn right on Skyline Dr. The driveway is the second on the right, about one mile up the road.

Pioneering Protection

In the past 15 years, the Northern Forest has been the site of some of the most dramatic and creative conservation successes in the United States. Here in Maine's vast North Woods alone, more than one million acres of forest have been protected by private conservation groups and state and federal agencies since 1997.

Some this newly conserved forest has been set aside as ecological reserves. Much of it, though, has been protected through conservation easements that protect the forest from residential and commercial development while allowing timber harvesting to continue. To further complement to these efforts, many landowners in the region have agreed to meet timber harvesting standards that are certified as sustainable by outside evaluators.

By working together and working creatively, people across the region are pioneering new strategies to secure the long-term health and integrity of both natural and human communities in the Northern Forest.

⌂ lodding   🍴 restaurant   artist gallery

Country Hearts Woodworking

Jim Donald creates pine pieces that are ready-to-finish. Visitors can find deacon benches, jelly cabinets, furniture for soft body dolls, and several shadow box sizes.

Open daily, call for hours.

207-645-4050 · 28 Lake School Road, Jay, ME · pdjdon71@adelphia.net

From Rt. 2 east, turn right on Rt. 4. In one mile turn right on Lake School Rd. and look for the giant wooden locomotive.

Imelda's Fabric and Designs

A converted racquet factory is the place to go for designer-style, custom-made, colorful apparel with detail stitching. Find

infant to plus sizes, as well as items for the family dog! Also find unique fabrics for home-decorating or dress-goods such as polar fleece and quilters' cottons.

Open Monday–Saturday 10 am–5 pm.

207-778-0665 · 5 Starks Road, New Sharon, ME janal@tdstelme.net

Tidbits
Moosehead Lake is the largest freshwater lake wholly contained in a single state in the nation.

 studio workshop

 craft marketplace

 special attraction

199

Maine Mountain Heritage: The Highlands

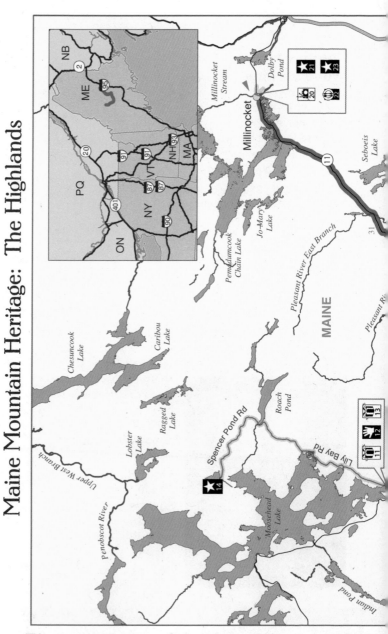

The main portion of the Maine Mountain Heritage

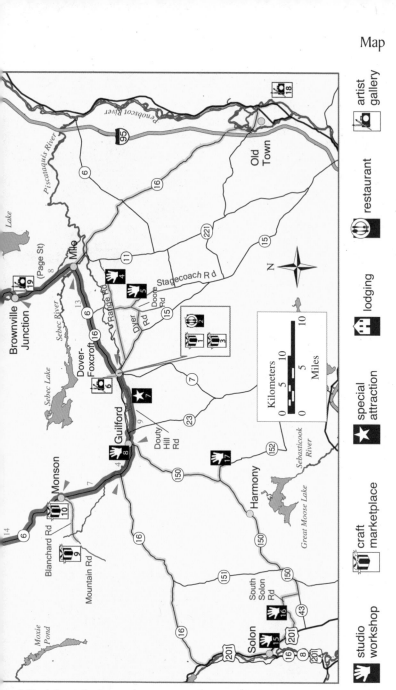

Map

artist gallery

restaurant

lodging

special attraction

craft marketplace

studio workshop

The Highlands loop is approximately 86 miles.

HIGHLANDS

Moosehead Furniture/ The Maine Highlands Guild Outlet

This retail outlet features Moosehead Furniture factory seconds and local products made by artisans in the Maine Highlands region who belong to the Maine Highlands Guild, a non-profit organization that promotes the work of local artisans. The variety of high-quality, hand-crafted items means that there is something for everyone: from pottery to photo prints, leather moccasins, pewter, jewelry, glass, flatware, candles, and exclusive furniture pieces. Displays explain how products are made and demonstrations and special events offer a glimpse of the artisan's task. Proceeds from the store support the nonprofit programs of The Maine Highlands.

Open Monday–Saturday 9 am–5 pm.

207-564-0041 • 97 East Main Street, Dover-Foxcroft, ME
www.themainehighlands-guild.org

Abel Bloods Pub/Restaurant

This sophisticated and eclectic eating and drinking establishment was named after the original settler of Piscataquis County. Visitors can find over 70 different beers and wines on the menu. Monthly, an art opening with complimentary appetizers, wine, and door prizes, provides an opportunity to meet the artist who will be displaying work in the restaurant the following month.

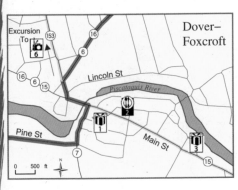

Open year-round. Art opening: first Wednesday of every month.

207-564-3177
100 East Main Street, Dover-Foxcroft, ME

 lodging   restaurant   artist gallery

Bob's Sugarhouse

Operating for more than 50 years, this sugarhouse makes pure Maine Maple Syrup. Take a tour of the building to get acquainted with the equipment and evaporating process from start to finish. Maple products and maple syrup can be found in the retail shop, attached to the evaporating and bottling room.

Open Monday–Friday 9 am–5 pm, and November–Christmas daily 9 am–7 pm.

**207-564-2145
252 East Maine Street,
Dover-Foxcroft, ME
www.mainemaplesyrup.com**

Northwoods Canoe Company

Inspired by the earliest inhabitants of the Maine woods who used birch bark to create canoes that were light, strong, and versatile, Rollin Thurlow builds and restores traditional wood and canvas canoes and repairs all kinds of wooden boats maintaining historic methods. Each craft is handmade with great care to the type and quality of material used.

Open Monday–Friday 8 am–5 pm.

**207-564-3667 • 336 Range Road, Atkinson, ME
www.woodencanoes.com**

Tidbits

Earmuffs were invented in by Chester Greenwood in Farmington, Maine in 1873.

 studio workshop

 craft marketplace

 special attraction

Island Falls Canoe Company

The wood canvas canoe, developed in the late 19th century directly from its birch bark predecessor, has never been exceeded for beauty, ease of handling, dependability, and proper flexibility. Built of renewable, organic materials, it is durable, easily repaired and built to last a lifetime. In this busy workshop, canoes are built by hand, using modern materials to update a generation old tradition. Artwork by Jerry Stelmok, a Maine native who lives and works in central Maine, depicts wilderness canoeing scenes, wildlife and lighthearted whimsical pieces.

Open weekdays 9 am–4 pm.

207-564-7612
220 Stagecoach Road,
Atkinson, ME
www.islandfalls.wcha.org

Green Door Gallery

Lost in the woods? Not a problem . . . Dave Lockwood makes custom lake maps of Maine on white pine and offers custom matting and framing. Each is carved to the depth of the water and labeled with name, scale of miles and direction finder. Specific locations, like the name of a camp or business can also be added. The Gallery is located next to the historic Blacksmith Museum.

Open May–December weekdays 11 am–5 pm, Saturday 11 am–4 pm.

207-564-8407 • 105 Dawes Road, Dover-Foxcroft, ME
www.downtownme.com/greendoorgallery

From Rts. 6/16, head north on Rt. 153; turn left onto Park Street and follow signs.

 lodging   restaurant   artist gallery

Stutzman's Farm Store

Find out about freshness at this third-generation vegetable farm! The store boasts a plentiful array of fresh hand-picked vegetables and fruits all summer long. Berries, peas, potatoes, lettuces, tomatoes, corn, squash, beet greens and other specialty vegetables compliment the fresh herb bread, pies, baked beans, jam, and other goodies made at the on-site bakery. Partake of cooking workshops throughout the summer or bring the kids and pick you own strawberries and pumpkins.

Open daily June–November 9 am–5 pm.
207-564-8596 · 891 Douty Hill Road, Sangerville, ME

Iron Art Forge

With smoke and hammer, blacksmith Gary Griffith pounds iron in his traditional forge into gifts and garden accessories. Member of The Maine Highlands Guild.

Open daily.

207-876-4569 Route 15, Guilford, ME
www. ironartforge.com

Tidbits

The northern terminus of the Appalachian Trail is on top of Mount Katahdin in Baxter State Park.

 studio workshop   craft marketplace   special attraction

Breakneck Ridge Farm

With a panoramic view of the Piscataquis River Valley and Russell Mountain as a backdrop, visitors will learn about raising American buffalo and fallow deer and collecting maple sap to transform into maple syrup. Feed the animals, taste the maple syrup over ice cream, or take a hay ride!

Open July–August and by appointment.
Tours: Adults $7, seniors $6, children (3-12) $5, under 3-free.
207-997-3922 • 160 Mountain Road, Blanchard Township, ME
www.breakneckridgefarm.com

Maine Highlands Guild

Tucked away in some of the most rural communities in the northeastern United States, the 80-plus members of the Maine Highlands Guild produce fine art and craft products ranging from furniture, to pottery, jewelry, baskets, quilts and much more.

Guild members work together to educate local children and adults about the culture and heritage of their region, while also collaborating to preserve traditional skills and help local artisans earn a living from their work. Membership is widely inclusive, but the Maine Highlands Guild brand name is reserved for craftspeople, artists, and traditional producers selected by a jury of qualified artisans, retail owners, and others. All members are offered guidance and assistance to help improve their products and business practices.

In partnership with Moosehead Furniture, the Guild opened a retail space in Dover-Foxcroft in 2004 where you can purchase member-made products or just learn more about their community programs. See listing on page 202 for details.

 lodging   restaurant   artist gallery

Lake Hebron Artisans

Only Maine-made handcrafted goods and food items fill this bright and colorful store. Visitors can find candles, wreaths, pottery, maple products, watercolors, photographs, rugs, pot holders, totes, gloves, hats, scarves, socks, pajamas, woolen bags from local sheep, traditional and contemporary baskets, stained glass, cushions, bird-houses, wooden bowls, dolls, leather deer-skin bags, scented pillows, slate paintings from local quarry, rake masks, traditional quilts, and art posters and cards.

Seasonal hours: open daily during summer, 9 am–5 pm, and during winter open Saturday and Sunday 10 am–3 pm.

207-997-3731 · 8 Greenville Road, Monson, ME
betty@midmaine.com

Maine Mountain Company Store

For over a decade, Sandra Dethlefsen has been harvesting flowers and herbs from her garden for a variety of all-natural bath and body products and candles. This retail store located in a log cabin showcases home and garden accessories made in Maine and houses the candle production and packaging facilities and office. An integral part of downtown Greenville, the grounds are also home to an organic farmers market throughout the summer and fall.

Open daily, check website or call for seasonal hours.

207-695-3926
17 Moosehead Lake Road,
Greenville, ME
www.mainemountain.com

 studio workshop

 craft marketplace

 special attraction

Rug with lake and mountains, the Moosehead Hooker

The Moosehead Hooker

Janice King makes and sells traditional hooked rugs and hand-split ash baskets. Her rugs feature Maine landscapes and are suitable for wall hangings. The ash for the baskets begin as a log in the shop out back and Janice can explain the production process which transitions the log into fine crafts.

Open Tuesday and Wednesday 10 am–3 pm or by appointment.
207-695-2768 · 203 Pritham Avenue, Greenville, ME
mooseheadhooker58@msn.com

Beyond the Bend

"Twigonometrist" Betsy Rockwell shapes and bends small wood into art forms. Cedar and other native wood is woven together to create life-size sculptures, trellises, arbors, panels, garden furniture, screens, or obelisks. Cement stepping stones and plaques are inlaid with stones from Moosehead Lake or may have real moose track impressions. Hanging and wall baskets woven together with red twig dogwood can hold plants or other items. Each cement

  lodging restaurant artist gallery

piece is unique, such as birdbaths with native leaf impressions or inlaid shells sitting on a birch or cedar stand.

Open daily April–October 8 am–5 pm and by appointment.

**207-695-2680 · 133 Lily Bay Road, Greenville, ME
beyondthbend@gwi.net**

EXCURSION TO SOLON AND CAMBRIDGE
looping back to route 16

Spencer Pond Camps

These camps are located in a region rich in cultural and natural history—fossils from the Devonian Era and artifacts from the Paleolithic people who lived here. The surrounding mountains figured prominently in Wabanaki folktales and fire rings are still visible along some lakeshores. The camps are located near the route that Thoreau followed on his first visit to the region in

the mid-1800s and the natural beauty inspires professional and amateur artists alike. Proprietors Bob Croce and Jill Martel promote the joy of discovery and a respect for natural areas.

Spencer Pond Camps

Open mid-May– mid-November.

207-843-5456 · 806 Spencer Pond Road, East Middlesex Township, ME · www.spencerpondcamps.com

Stained Glass Wizard

It feels like magic in this studio . . . the custom-designed sun catchers, clocks, ornaments, and jewelry boxes made by Chuck Aloes brighten any corner.

Open daily 8 am–4:30 pm.

**207-643-2666 · 417 South Main Street/Route 201, Solon, ME
www.stainedglasswizard.com**

Take Rt. 16 west, then south on Rt. 201.

 studio workshop

 craft marketplace

special attraction

South Solon Woodworks

Woodworker Roy Alan Slamm designs and creates

contemporary furniture and objects as well as manufactures small runs of hardwood objects for various Maine businesses. "My non-traditional work tends to be one of a kind, with an artistic tendency."

Open Tuesday & Wednesday 9 am–4 pm.

207-643-2346 · 906 South Solon Road, Solon, ME
royslamm@kynd.net

Continue south on Rt. 201 then turn left (east) on Rt. 43 and left on South Solon Road.

Erda

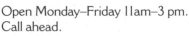

Erda makes artsy handbags, drawing on traditional ideas and adding a contemporary twist. Use of tapestry fabrics, silks—even deerskin!—result in styles ranging from medieval to uptown gallery. "We have the fringy stuff, but also sleek, sculptural [bags]. We add embellishments such as fossil ivory, handmade pewter pendants, and gemstones." For the truly fashionable, check out the line of photo albums, checkbook covers, address books, and journals, especially the items made out of recycled denim jeans, with real belts!

Open Monday–Friday 11am–3 pm.
Call ahead.

207-277-5115 · 375 Ripley Road (Route 152), Cambridge, ME
www.ErdaLeather.com

Continue east on Rt. 43 to the junction with Rt. 150, head north. Return to the remainder of the main loop on Rt. 150 north, turning right (east) on Rt. 16 in Guilford.

 lodging   restaurant   artist gallery

Thoreau & The Maine Woods

"Not only for strength, but for beauty, the poet must, from time to time travel the logger's path and the Indian's trail, to drink at some new and more bracing fountain of the Muses, far in the recesses of the wilderness."

—Henry David Thoreau, The Maine Woods

Henry David Thoreau's journeys through the Maine woods in 1846, 1853 and 1856 inspired memorable portraits of the wilderness to be found beyond the trappings of the industrial and agrarian economies emerging along the forest edges.

Thoreau's travels took him to Moosehead and Chesuncook lakes, along the Penobscot and Allagash rivers, and to the slopes of Maine's tallest mountain, Katahdin. Captured in his book The Maine Woods, *his reflections on these journeys sowed some of the early seeds of the modern conservation movement and inspired countless explorers, wanderers, and thinkers to venture into the woods in search of inspiration and communion with nature.*

"On tops of mountains, as everywhere to hopeful souls, it is always morning."

Wabanaki Arts Center Gallery/Maine Indian Basketmakers Alliance

This Gallery carries the work of over 100 tribal artisans—each piece a unique representation of the rich culture and traditions practiced by the members of Maine's Maliseet, Micmac, Passamaquodddy and Penobscot Tribes. Visitors can find Brown Ash and Sweetgrass baskets, traditional carved root clubs and canes, carved rattles and talking sticks, beadwork, porcupine quill jewelry, handmade dolls, birch bark baskets, pack baskets, potato baskets, and utility baskets. The gallery supports the nonprofit programs of the Maine Indian Basketmakers Alliance.

Open Monday–Saturday 10 am–5 pm.

207-827-0391 · 240 Maine Street, Old Town, ME
www.maineindianbaskets.org

Head South on Rt. 16 from Milo. After crossing I-95, turn left on Route 43. Continue 3.5 miles into Old Town. Arts Center is on the left.

 studio
workshop

 craft
marketplace

 special
attraction

211

Paradox on Page

Artfully eclectic, this gallery features quality handmade items from local and not-so-local artists. Jewelry, pottery, wood sculpture, fiber art, photography, and glass are just a few of the unusual things visitors will find. Amy and Dean Rouse create colorful stemware in the adjacent Glass Paradox studio, where visitors can see them working on new pieces. Say hello to Jessie and Tessie, the resident cats who greet gallery customers.

Open Wednesday–Saturday 10 am–5 pm, Sunday 12 pm–5 pm.

207-965-8200 · 67 Page Street, Brownville Junction, ME
glass@glassparadox.com

In Brownville Junction, turn right onto Payne Street then left onto Page Street.

Memories of Maine Gallery

Visitors can find artwork, nature photography, antiques, estate jewelry, magnets, greeting cards, and collectibles in this gallery. Jean McLean-Corocran showcases the Maine coast, Mount Katahdin, wildflowers, moose, wild berries, and the deep woods. A custom frame shop also produces unique designer sports mats for basketball, football, soccer, golf, baseball, and hockey, as well as special occasions. Member of The Maine Highlands Guild.

Open Monday–Friday 10 am–5 pm, Saturday 10 am–4 pm.

207-723-4834 · 80 Penobscot Avenue, Millinocket, ME
www.memoriesofmaine.com

 lodging   restaurant   artist gallery

New England Outdoor Center

A family resort, the Center's rafting outings provides a range of north woods experiences: the roller coaster waves of the Kennebec River; breathtaking beauty and technical challenge of the Penobscot; or brave the wild and woolly Dead River! Visitors will also find spectacular foliage in the fall and guaranteed big water fun from April to mid-October. The Center has three different locations, Kennebec Base, Penobscot Base, and Twin Pine Camps.

Open year-round.

207-723-5438 • 800-766-7238
Medway Road, Millinocket, ME • www.neoc.com

River Driver

As one of the sites of the New England Outdoor Center, this retreat center has it all—rustic to deluxe lakeside cabins, modern conference facilities, world class dining and extensive outdoor recreational programs—all in the beautiful wilderness setting of Northern Maine.

Open daily Summer/Winter: 6 am–12 am.
Spring/Fall: 8 am–8 pm.

207-723-8475 • 800-766-7238
Medway Road, Millinocket, ME • www.neoc.com

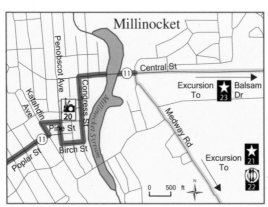

 studio
workshop

 craft
marketplace

 special
attraction

Baxter State Park

"Man is born to die, his works are short-lived. Buildings crumble, monuments decay, wealth vanishes. But Katahdin in all its glory, forever shall remain the mountain of the people of Maine."

With these words, former Governor Percival Baxter presented the people of Maine the magnificent gift and the tremendous responsibility of caring for the jewel of the North Woods: Baxter State Park.

Beginning in 1930 with the purchase of 6,000 acres of land including Maine's highest peak, Mount Katahdin, Baxter spent 32 years piecing together the 200,000-acre park that bears his name. In addition to Katahdin, Baxter State Park includes more than 40 peaks and ridges, and over 180 miles of trails, making it a widely popular destination for hikers, climbers and naturalists.

Despite its popularity, in keeping with the conditions of Baxter's gift, the park is maintained primarily as a wilderness with recreational purposes given secondary importance to the primary objective of keeping the area "Forever Wild."

Entry to and camping in Baxter State Park are tightly managed so be sure to call ahead before visiting—(207) 723-5140.

Baxter State Park

Katahdin, the northern terminus of the Appalachian Trail, is an awesome, inspiring sight. At 5268 feet, the mountain summit is the most difficult non-technical climb in the East. Trails have a tendency to go straight up—the most spectacular route involves taking the mile-long "Knife's Edge," which drops 2,000 feet on either side of the trail. To camp or access the park, come early in the day as daily quotas limit the number of park-goers.

207-723-5140 · 64 Balsam Drive, Millinocket, ME
www.baxterstateparkauthority.com

 lodging   restaurant   artist gallery

Crown of Maine

In far northern Maine, discover a culture where people hold close ties to the land, to their French-Canadian neighbors, and to their own heritage. The Crown of Maine Tour guides you to the hidden treasures of a truly special place.

A stay at the historic 1865 Sewall House Retreat in Island Falls, followed by a gourmet brunch and sampling of local art at the Courtyard Café in Houlton, will prepare you to head north toward Presque Isle and the Reed Art Gallery at the local University of Maine campus. The open views across miles and miles of farm fields here in the heart of Maine's potato country are a rare treat after a long journey through the forest.

Photo by Jay Ericson

From Presque Isle, follow picturesque country roads on a winding circuit to Caribou, where offerings include a fine art studio, an alpaca farm, and the Nylander Museum of Natural History. On the way you'll discover a working farm offering traditional local crafts, and an artist's studio that serves as a starting point for snowshoe trips and orchid tours, depending on the season. Consider a side trip to the towns of Stockholm and New Sweden, and notice the distinctive flags and architecture of the Swedish Colony established here in 1870.

Continuing north to the St. John Valley, immerse yourself in a culture that has evolved since the first French-Acadian settlers arrived in the 1780s. As you tour the local artist and craft venues, watch for Acadian sites and attractions, listen for the "Valley French" spoken by many local residents, and stop into a local restaurant to sample traditional St. John Valley buckwheat pancakes, or *ployes*.

From the small college of town of Fort Kent, you'll plunge back into the heart of the Maine Woods. This final leg of the tour carries you through a region where the Deep in the Woods Gift Shop is aptly named, and where the "moose crossing" signs mean what they say. Round out your trip with a visit to the Patten Lumbermen's Museum with its complex of treasures from a time when trees were felled by axe and hauled by horse.

Follow this tour through rolling farmlands and wild forests to uncover the gems and jewels in the Crown of Maine Tour.

Cultural Heritage Profile

La Culture Acadienne du Maine

As you approach the farthest reaches of northern Maine, don't be concerned when you notice business people speaking French with their customers or signs written in both French and English. You haven't accidentally crossed the border into Quebec; you've entered the Acadian communities of the St. John River Valley.

Maine's Acadians are descended from French ancestors who in the 1600s settled along the coast of Nova Scotia—then known as Acadia. In the years before the American Revolution, both France and England held a claim to this area, and in 1755 the English deported thousands of French settlers. While many were shipped directly to the British Colonies, others fled in search of homelands where they could maintain their Acadian identity.

Some of those who fled settled in Louisiana—the ancestors of today's Cajuns. Others traveled to Quebec. During the 1780s, a small group of Acadian families settled along the St. John River.

More than 200 years later, Acadian culture and traditions continue to thrive along the river and in the "back settlements" of the St. John Valley. Throughout the region you'll hear people young and old speaking Valley French—a mixture of traditional French and English with some Quebecois phrases added. Traditional arts and folkways ranging from woodcarving to snowshoe making, rug weaving, gardening, singing, and fiddling are passed down from generation to generation. Throughout the Valley, Acadians share religious traditions, connections with the river and the land, and knowledge of the deportation story of their ancestors.

Each summer, the Acadian Festival celebrates this rich heritage and culture of the St. John Valley. If your visit doesn't coincide with the festival, though, watch for numerous Acadian sites including historic churches, museums, and traditional buildings along US Route 1. To learn more, contact the Maine Acadian Heritage Council at 207-728-6826.

Crown of Maine

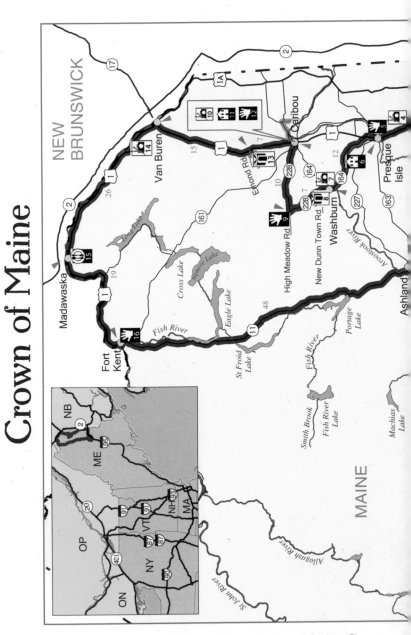

The main portion of the Crown o

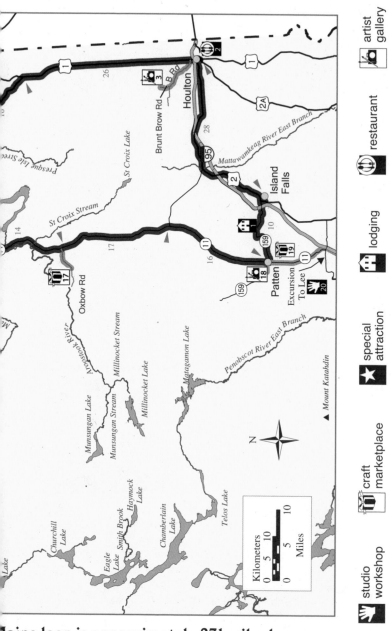

artist gallery

restaurant

lodging

special attraction

craft marketplace

studio workshop

Houlton

Island Falls

Patten

Excursion To Lee

Brunt Brow Rd

B. Rd

Oxbow Rd

St Croix Lake

St Croix Stream

Presque Isle Stream

Mattawamkeag River East Branch

Penobscot River East Branch

Munsungan Lake

Munsungan Stream

Millinocket Stream

Millinocket Lake

Matagamon Lake

Churchill Lake

Eagle Lake

Smith Brook

Haymock Lake

Chamberlain Lake

Telos Lake

Aroostook River

Mount Katahdin

N

Kilometers

0   5   10

0   5   10

Miles

... laine loop is approximately 271 miles long.

ISLAND FALLS

Sewall House Retreat

Built in 1865, this building on the National Register of Historic Places served as the community's first post office and inn. For lovers of history, antiques, and books, the house offers many treasures. The décor reflects the era and region where the owner's great-grandfather's family was among the first settlers. Theodore Roosevelt also stayed as a student at Harvard College in an attempt to overcome a lifelong asthma affliction. His adventures in the north woods of climbing Katahdin and visiting loggers are portrayed. Continuing this healing tradition, the House operates as a retreat offering morning hatha/astanga yoga and afternoon Kundalini yoga practice.

Open June 15–Columbus Day and during Christmas holiday. Yoga classes held daily 8:30 am & 5 pm. Call ahead.

207-463-3428 • 888-235-2395
1027 Crystal Road, Island Falls, ME • www.sewallhouse.com

The Courtyard Café

An ongoing exhibit of local artwork is featured in this intimate café. Stop by for a gourmet meal.

Open Monday–Friday 11 am–2 pm, Tuesday–Thursday 5 pm–8 pm, Friday–Saturday 5 pm–9 pm. Reservations not required, but suggested.

207-532-0787
61 Main Street, Houlton, ME
www.thecourtyardcafe.biz

Hines Stonework

Glenn and Diane Hines sculpt in clay and cast in bronze and reinforced concrete. Visitors can gaze on extraordinary wildlife and figurative sculpture and large memorial sculptures made in the studio. Large bronze sculptures, stonewalls, and beautiful buildings grace the property. "We have been working on this art for 30 years. Northern Maine has exceptional beauty, and life here is good."

Open March–November: Monday–Friday daylight hours.

207-532-4141 • 317 Burnt Brow Road, Hammond, ME

 lodging   restaurant   artist gallery

Swedish Colony

On June 25, 1870, 50 men, women, and children departed their native Sweden for new lives in Maine's North Woods. With the promise of 100 acres of forest (with five acres cleared) for each family, these hardy settlers were recruited to establish a new agricultural settlement in the virgin forest northwest of Caribou.

As word of their success circulated back to Sweden, hundreds more immigrants made the journey to northern Maine seeking land, work and opportunity. By 1873 there were 1,500 Swedes in Maine. The population of the Swedish Colony itself had grown to 600 with 2,200 acres of forest felled and nearly 1,500 acres cleared for agriculture. In 1895 the town of New Sweden was incorporated as the center of the growing community.

The influence of the Swedish Colony remains strong today. In 2000, signs were erected on main roads entering the area to highlight its Swedish heritage. Each summer, residents and visitors gather for the traditional Swedish Midsommar Celebration, when all local Swedish museums and historic sites are open to the public.

Reed Art Gallery, University of Maine at Presque Isle

On the campus of the University of Maine at Presque Isle, this gallery is the premier venue for visual arts in northern Maine. Annually, eight exhibitions are shown of work by state and nationally known contemporary and historical artists.

Open Monday–Saturday 10 am–5 pm.
Closed during college vacations.

207-768-9453 · 181 Main Street, Campus Center, Presque Isle, ME · www.umpi.maine.edu

studio workshop

craft marketplace

special attraction

223

The Space Between

Elizabeth Punches is a professional exhibiting artist nationwide and operates out of her studio and gallery, The Space Between. Her work can be seen on permanent display at Virginia Intermont College in Bristol, Virginia, Caroline's LLC in Abingdon, VA, The Richmond Museum of Fina Art in Richmond, VA and in private collections in many states. All work created in the last two years was executed in her studio found at The Space Between, where she also maintains a small gallery displaying her work as well as several other artists working in Aroostook County, Maine. "Most often, I use a very old traditional method of painting, involving underpaintings, hand mixed glazes, and thick bodied paint application. Although I use these traditional elements, I am classified as a contemporary painter because of my content, composition, and approach."

Open year–round, please call for an appointment.

207-764-2911 or 866-847-6031
396 Main Street, Presque Isle, ME • zabethanne@aol.com

Rum Rapids Inn

Built in the 1830s on the banks of the Aroostook River, this inn is the oldest standing home in northern Maine. Once residence to loyalists, visitors can now enjoy the 19th-century flower garden, relax on the porch or watch the Rum Rapids just feet away from the living room! Afternoon tea, candlelit dinners, spa, Swedish wood-fired sauna and solar cottages make this a destination in all seasons.

Open daily 10 am–6 pm.

207-455-8096 • 26 Rum Rapids Drive, Washburn, ME
www.rumrapidsinn.com

Five miles after turn off Rt. 1 in Presque Isle.
On left, small sign at top of driveway.

Stretching 40 miles from Presque Isle to Houlton, the Maine Solar System Model is the world's largest complete three-dimensional scale model of the solar system. Watch for models of planets strategically placed along US Route 1 between the two communities.

Tidbits

 lodging   restaurant   artist gallery

Salmon Brook Historical Society of Washburn

 Handmade a century ago, this museum showcases an extensive collection of old machinery and equipment, including rare pottery and iron, copper and brass culinary items. "The Fox's Den" displays fine craftsman chests, numerous types of wooden plans, and rare shop tools.

Open May–October: Saturday–Sunday 1 pm–4 pm, Wednesday 8 am–11 am or by appointment.

207-455-4339 · 17 Main Street, Washburn, ME
smnbrkhs@mfx.net

Knot-II-Bragg Farm

Meet Natalia Bragg who gardens and tends to the animals on this farm. Her shop reflects local and regional crafts products, as well as the traditions that have been passed down for generations. Look for applewood pencils, soaps, wooden animals, walking sticks, traditional bone and stone charms, as well as bone stone, and quill earrings, necklaces and bracelets. Visitors will find unique stickwood furniture, wreaths, dried flowers, grasses and a selection of traditional herbal products from northern Maine.

Open June 1–October 31: Tuesday–Saturday 10 am–5 pm. Call ahead.

207-455-8386 · 469 New Dunn Town Rd., Wade, ME
www.knotiibragg.com

Turn left onto Bridge Street at the library and cross bridge. At the Methodist Church turn left onto Church Street (non-standard intersection). Where Church Street dead ends on New Dunn Town Road, turn right. The farm is approximately 3 miles from town on the right.

 studio workshop

 craft marketplace

 special attraction

Woods Edge Gallery

A small art gallery doubles as a studio space where Richard Clark's paintings highlight the natural landscape of Aroostook county. In winter, the gallery serves as the starting point for a network of snowshoe trails connected to Maine public reserve lands. In spring and early summer, it is the meeting place for tours of orchid and other rare plant stations.

Open Tuesday–Saturday 1 pm–5 pm.

207-455-8359 • 265 High Meadow Road, Perham, ME

The Nylander Museum

Olof O. Nylander (1864-1943) was a Swedish immigrant, self-taught natural historian and published scientist. Visitors to the Museum can find his vast collections of rocks, minerals, fossils, Native American stone tools, mounted Maine animals, marine shells, photographs, archival copies, and butterflies. The giftshop or natural history library is also a delight. Outside the museum, visitors can stroll through the garden of traditional and native medicinal plants.

Open Memorial Day–Labor Day: Tuesday–Saturday 12:30 pm–4:30 pm. Other days and times by appointment. Free admission, donations accepted.

207-493-4209 • 657 Main Street, Caribou, ME www.nylandermuseum.org

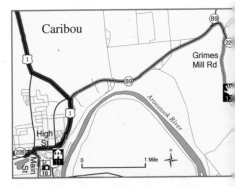

Maine's Aroostook County is the largest county in the United States east of the Mississippi River.

Tidbits

226

 lodging   restaurant   artist gallery

The Old Iron Inn B&B

This small, European-style bed and breakfast boasts an extensive collection of antique irons. Each of the four rooms is individually decorated with antique furniture. Innkeeper Kate McCartney hosts a music night with area musicians on the third Friday of each month.

Open daily.

207-492-4766 · 155 High Street, Caribou, ME
www.oldironinn.com

AzureWing Studio

Visit this studio/gallery in a 1935 cottage farmhouse on an 84-

acre wooded and pastured farm. Linda Crane paints highly realistic botanical subjects, sky- and landscapes, as well as still-life subjects, on specially prepared water color paper. Prints and cards are available in the studio/gallery as well as handmade spinning and knitting accessories, jewelry, and 1:12 scale paintings.

Open seasonally May– December: Thursday– Saturday 10 am–5 pm, except for show or workshop weekends. Other times by appointment.

207-496-3650 · 168 Grimes Mill Road, Caribou, ME
www.azurewingstudio.com

North Woods Farm Fiber Company

Teri and Larry Gabric raise alpacas and Shetland sheep. Visitors can see the animals in this picturesque setting, tour their fiber processing mill, or sort through yarn, fleece or finished handwoven and knitted products, such as mittens.

Open Monday–Saturday 10 am–4 pm, please call ahead.

207-498-3293 · 145 Emond Road, Caribou, ME
www.northwoodsfarm.com

 studio
workshop

 craft
marketplace

 special
attraction

A Skiing Lifestyle

Swedish immigrants who settled in Maine in the 1870s found it an ideal place to continue a favorite aspect of life back in Europe: cross country skiing. In 1999 the Maine Winter Sports Center was created to reestablish that skiing lifestyle in communities across the state.

In the past five years, sports center staff and volunteers have built cross-country ski trails and helped integrate skiing into school curricula in communities across Aroostook County and the rest of the state. They also have established Aroostook County as a world-class destination for recreational and competitive skiing by developing the 10th Mountain Center in Fort Kent and the Nordic Heritage Center in Presque Isle. These new training and touring facilities are considered among the finest in the world, and the 10th Mountain Center already has hosted major national and international ski competitions.

Community trails the Maine Winter Sports Center has developed are open to the public year round and free of charge for non-motorized use. The 10th Mountain Center and Nordic Heritage Center trails are free as well. Stop by to explore the trails and the heritage of skiing in the Northern Forest. Visit www.mainewsc.org for more information.

Acadian Village

14

This village encompasses 16 reconstructed and fully furnished buildings dating from the 1700s–1900s. Visitors can experience an Acadian mode of living in the St John Valley and find handmade quilts and baskets in the country gift store

Open daily June 15–September 15, 12 noon–5 pm.
For special tours of 10 or more, open May 31–October 1.
$4.50 adults $2.50 students under 12.

207-868-5042 or 207-868-2691 • Route 1, Van Buren, ME
www.themainelink.com/acadianvillage

  lodging   restaurant   artist gallery

Cafe de la Place

This lively gallery offers a multi-cultural respite in the middle

of town. Monthly exhibits feature local artistry, such as photography, paintings, arts, crafts and pieces of sicla commentary. The pleasant atmosphere, especially from a couch overlooking the St. John Valley, is accompanied by the smell of fresh coffee and homemade pastries. The French language rolls easily off the tongue of the clientele, giving off a warm Parisian flair.

Open Monday–Friday 5 am–2 pm. Closed weekends.
207-728-0944 • 285 Main Street, Madawaska, ME

Artist At Work

Enormous picture windows facade this studio overflowing with paintbrushes, easels, stools, drapery, local antiques, a variety of still life set ups, shelves of art books and cast moldings. Visitors can see and inquire about purchasing the work of Therese Provenzano as well as the work of her students.

Open Thursday 3 pm–8:30 pm,
Saturday 10 am–3:30 pm, call ahead.

207-834-4ART • 78 East Main Street, Fort Kent, ME
www.artistatworkstudio.com

OxBow Wreaths Deep In The Woods Gift Shop

Since 1986, award-winning balsam fir wreaths from this farm have graced homes across the country. Fresh Christmas trees are also a favorite and the gift shop is filled with quilts, jams, jellies, muffin mixes, soaps, and candles made by Aroostook county artisans.

Open Thursday–Monday 12 noon–7 pm.
November–December daily 7 am–7 pm.

207-435-6171 • 685 OxBow Road
Oxbow, ME • www.deepinthewoods.org

 studio workshop

 craft marketplace

 special attraction

229

The Patten Lumbermen's Museum

This Museum presents a nostalgic view of the bygone lumber days of the "Great North Woods." Nine buildings, 5000

artifacts, 1000 early logging photos, two loghaulers, and a recreated logging camp illustrates the hard work, life, and leisure times of the men who perfected the "art of logging."

Open any holidays and Mondays
July 1–August 31:
Tuesday–Sunday
10 am–4 pm. Memorial Day–June 30 & September 1–
Columbus Day: Friday–Sunday 10 am–4 pm.
Adults $7, seniors $6, children 6–11 $2, children under 6 free; group rates available by request.

207-528-2650 • 25 Waters Road, Patten, ME
www.lumbermensmuseum.org

Potato Empire

While trees clearly dominate the landscape in most of the Northern Forest, here in the northern reaches of Maine they share the land with a shorter, bushier cousin—the potato.

For more than 200 years, potato farming has been part of the culture and economy of Aroostook County, making Maine the nation's leading producer until it 1958. While the number of farms and farmers has declined since then, potato fields still dominate much of the landscape from Houlton to Madawaska. Low buildings that look like roofs sitting on the ground are actually potato houses used to store crops in the cool earth. Depending on the season, you may enjoy the spectacle of potato blossoms stretching in all directions, or opportunities to purchase young "new potatoes" from local farmers.

Despite the challenges, today many local farmers are experimenting with organic practices and diversified crops to ensure the future of farming in Aroostook County.

 lodging   restaurant   artist gallery

Theriault Flies

19

Anything you've ever wanted for fishing can be found at this store. Find flies galore and fly tying material from birds, llamas, and goats raised by Alvin Theriault. Visitors will enjoy the drive leading to the shop past picturesque pastures and animals.

Open Tuesday–Saturday 11 am–6 pm.

207-365-4007 · 1135 Station Road, Stacyville, ME
www.theriaultflies.com

EXCURSION TO LEE

Dragonfly Instruments
Damselfly Photographic Studio

20

Instruments of all shapes and sizes come to life in this workshop and showroom. Thomas Knowles gives life to guitars, dulcimers, banjos, violins, mandolins, and bousouki

using local woods—spruce, cedar, maple, cherry, and black locust. Visitors can also find stunning photographs on display.

Open Fall/Winter: Almost always available, call ahead.

207-738-4696
53 Slipper Ridge, Lee, ME
dragonflyinc@pivot.net

Continue South on Rt. 11 to Sherman, then take I-95 South. Exit in Lincoln, and travel east on Rt. 6. At intersection with Rt. 168, turn right onto Arab Rd. Travel one mile. Turn right onto Slipper Ridge. Bear left and travel to end.

studio
workshop

craft
marketplace

special
attraction

Chapter
11

Coastal Treasures

From the busy islands off of Acadia National Park to the remote fishing villages and inland lakes along the border with New Brunswick, the Coastal Treasures Tour traces a ribbon between the vast Northern Forest to the west and the wide Atlantic Ocean to the east. Tucked along the coves and small villages on the way, you'll find fine art and handmade crafts that reflect the dual influences of forest and sea.

The route begins on Deer Isle, home of the world-renowned Haystack Mountain School of Craft and myriad studios and galleries that have been inspired and influenced by the school's creative presence. Back on the mainland you'll find one-of-a-kind textiles featured in several galleries on the Blue Hill Peninsula,

Photos by: Jerry & Marcy Monkman/EcoPhotography.com

before heading up US Route 1 toward Acadia National Park and the uncrowded pleasures of Washington County—known locally as Sunrise County for its distinction as the site of the most easterly point of land in the United States.

The trip to Mount Desert Island and the national park is rewarded by hiking and site seeing amidst the stunning landscapes as well as shops, restaurants, and magnificent museums exploring the region's natural history and Native American cultures. Continuing north on Route 1, past the turn off to the park, you'll discover a land beyond the reach of most tourists—one featuring small villages, a remote and rocky shoreline, seemingly endless blueberry barrens, and the hidden art and craft treasures of far Downeast Maine. Along the way you'll find hand-molded bronze bells, fine furniture, magnificent hand-turned garden containers, woodcarvings, rugs, pottery, fine art galleries, and even a blueberry-shaped blueberry shop.

Round out your trip with a visit to the Downeast Heritage Center in Calais with its interpretive exhibits exploring local history and culture, and a gift shop featuring handmade local products. Finally, head back into the forest to visit Bill Shamel's Boat and Canoe Works in Grand Lake Stream—a tiny forest community named after its legendary salmon stream.

Here at the eastern edge of the Northern Forest, enjoy the confluence of forest and maritime cultures on the Coastal Treasures Tour.

233

Cultural Heritage Profile

Cross of Cultures

As the site of the first real effort to create a permanent European settlement in the New World, St. Croix Island is a landmark in the history of interaction among the French, the English, and Native Americans in the region the French called L'Acadie, and that we now know as Maine and the Canadian Maritimes.

In 1604, prior to the creation of English settlements in Jamestown or Plymouth, a French expedition led by Pierre Dugua chose St. Croix Island, in the river of the same name, as the site for a permanent settlement. Arriving in early summer, the group of nearly 80 men quickly built houses, storage buildings, and a church, and planted gardens. Despite their efforts, a shortage of fresh food during the winter led to an outbreak of scurvy that

Photo by: Jerry & Marcy Monkman/EcoPhotography.com

killed nearly half the group. The following summer, they moved the settlement across the Bay of Fundy to a new location at Port Royal. This settlement also was destined to fail when the French crown revoked Dugua's charter in 1607.

Despite its failures, this venture led to the production of the first detailed European map of the Gulf of Maine by cartographer Samuel De Champlain. The expedition also resulted in some of the earliest significant trade and interaction between the Europeans and the region's native tribes, and marked the beginning of an enduring French presence in the area.

Today, the public can explore this crucial moment in the early relations between European and Native American cultures. St. Croix Island itself was declared a National Monument in 1949, and since 1984 has been managed by the National Park Service as an International Historic Site. In 2004, the Downeast Heritage Museum in Calais opened with a series of exhibits featuring the history of the region's Native American population and the French experience at St. Croix Island.

The Heritage Museum also features a gift shop with handmade local products, public programs on the region's natural and human history, and a clearinghouse of information about cultural attractions and heritage resources in Downeast Maine. See page 255 for contact information.

Coastal Treasures

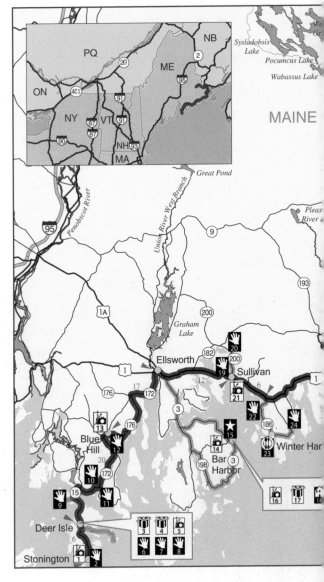

The main portion of the Coastal Treasu

lodging

restaurant

artist gallery

studio workshop

craft marketplace

special attraction

op is approximately 194 miles long.

STONINGTON

D. Mortenson Gallery

Nestled downtown in this tiny fishing village, this gallery's backyard is the ocean. Original paintings in watercolor and oil, photography, sculpture, and prints by classically-trained artist Debi Mortenson grace her gallery. Visitors can also find original art notecards, postcards, t-shirts, and miscellaneous collectibles.

Open in-season: Thursday–Tuesday 11 am–6 pm.
Off-season: Friday–Monday 12 noon–5 pm.

207-367-5875 · 10 West Main St., Stonington, ME
www.debimortenson.com

Geoffrey Warner Studio

Visitors can find handmade furniture and paintings of coastal Maine in this gallery. For over 25 years, Geoffrey Warner has been designing and building custom cabinetry and fine furniture to suit customer's special needs.

Open daily.

207-367-6555 · 43 North Main Street, Stonington, ME
www.geoffreywarnerstudio.com

The term "Downeast" refers to the practice of sailing downwind, in an easterly direction, with the prevailing westerly winds at your back.

Tidbits

 lodging   restaurant   artist gallery

Haystack Mountain School of Crafts

People travel across the globe to nurture creativity, reassess their work and lives, and delve into the unknown at the Haystack Mountain School of Crafts.

Built on a cliff overlooking Jericho Bay in the Atlantic Ocean, Haystack's quiet, 40-acre campus inspires students and instructors alike. Intensive, studio-based workshops foster work with clay, glass, metals, paper, blacksmithing, weaving, and wood, with

programs ranging from short workshops to three-week sessions for beginners and professionals. The Haystack experience is the combined result of renowned teachers, intensive studio time, exploration of other art forms including music and dance, a diverse student body, and an unforgettable exposure to creative ideas.

Haystack is open June–August, and visitors are welcome to attend the "End of Session Auction." Call 207-348-2306 or visit www.haystack-mtn.org for schedule and fee. The Blue Heron Gallery features contemporary crafts by Haystack faculty and students (see below).

Blue Heron Gallery

Located in a classic New England barn, this gallery shows the work of the Haystack School of Crafts faculty—past and present. Pieces are featured during the teaching session, including extraordinary models of contemporary clay, glass, wood, fiber, metal, jewelry, paper, and handmade books. Traditional work is honored along with contemporary use of traditional materials, each piece the product of the artist's inspiration.

Open June–September: Sunday–Monday 1 pm–5:30 pm, Tuesday–Saturday 10 am–5:30 pm.

207-348-6051 · 22 Church Street, Deer Isle, ME
www.blueheron.com

 studio
workshop

 craft
marketplace

 special
attraction

239

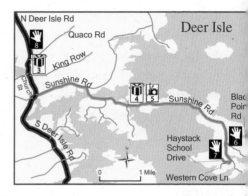

Deer Isle

Nervous Nellie's Jams & Jellies

Watch the jam-makers at work! Every jar is poured, capped, and labeled by hand, while the heavenly scent of berries bubbling in the kettle is carried on the sea breeze. Cooking takes place most weekday mornings and observers are welcome. In the summer, free samples of all 15 flavors are available in the shop and the Mountainville Cafe serves coffee, tea, and homemade scones—with plenty of jam, of course!

Open daily May–October 9 am–5 pm.
Partially Handicapped Accessible.

800-777-6845 · 598 Sunshine Road, Deer Isle, ME
www.nervousnellies.com

Peter Beerits Sculpture

More than 60 whimsical sculptures made of native pine and metal artifacts inhabit the surrounding meadows, decks, and spruce woods. Visitors will be delighted to find a sheep made out of an enormous Sears & Roebuck rural delivery mailbox or a 5-foot high baby giraffe on wheels, like a child's pull toy. In a grove of spruces stands a façade—drawbridge and all—of the Grail castle, complete with archers, heralds, maids, and merrymakers.

Open year-round.
Partially Handicapped Accessible.

800-777-6845
600 Sunshine Road, Deer Isle, ME
www.nervousnellies.com

 lodging   restaurant   artist gallery

Conary Cove Glass Works

Glistening with reflections from the sun and sea, glass bead

Conary Cove necklace close-up

necklaces and earrings are made by Joleen Dodge in this studio. Every set is flame worked with amoretti glass. "Each handmade bead that I create is mysteriously unique and its beauty is inspired by the islands I am blessed to live upon."

Open Saturday–Sunday 9 am–5 pm,
or by chance or appointment.

207-348-9402 · 3 Black Point Road, Deer Isle, ME

Haystack Mountain School of Crafts

People from all over the world attend this international craft school to develop and discover skills, nurture creativity, and push into the unknown. On its 40-acre campus overlooking Jericho Bay in the Atlantic Ocean, Haystack offers intensive, studio-based workshops in a variety of media, including clay, glass, metals, paper, blacksmithing, weaving, and woodworking. Programs range from short workshops to three-week sessions, for beginners to advanced professionals. Visitors can join an organized tour or attend the "End of Session Auction." Visit the Blue Heron Gallery to see fine contemporary crafts by past and present faculty and students.

Open June–August.
Tours: Wednesdays 1 pm.
Call for schedule and fee.
Partially Handicapped Accessible.

207-348-2306 · 89 Haystack School Drive, Deer Isle, ME
www.haystack-mtn.org

 studio workshop    craft marketplace   special attraction   241

Frederica Marshall Studio

In an 1830s Sea Captain's house, workshops and classes in Oriental Brush Painting, Japanese Paper Marbling and Watercolor are taught. Visitors can find original Sumi-e and watercolors of Maine. Oriental name seals are custom carved and small wooden articles and handmade brushes are made on site.

Open June–September: 12 noon–5 pm, Tuesday–Saturday by chance or appointment. Fee for classes.

207-348-2782
81 North Deer Isle Road, Deer Isle, ME
www.fredericamarshall.com

Dream Weaver

Mary Eaton creates sweaters and scarves from a variety of fibers, including the most sought-after rayon chenille because of its comfort and color saturation. She has three to four knitting machines working most of the time and a production loom wrapped up and ready to weave. Visitors can find over 100 beaded Christmas ornaments as well as watercolors and oil paintings and multiple shelves of handknitting yarns.

Open April–December, Monday–Saturday 10 am–5 pm. Closed Sunday.

207-348-6294 • 222 Blastow Cove Road, Little Deer Isle, ME
www.dreamweavermaine.com

After crossing the bridge onto Little Deer Isle, Turn Right onto Eggemoggin Rd. From there, follow the signs to Dream Weaver Studio.

Machias, Maine, was the site of the first naval battle of the Revolutionary War.

Tidbits

 lodging   restaurant   artist gallery

Where the Sun Always Rises

The striking red and white stripes of West Quoddy Head Light mark the most easterly point of land in the United States.

Why is the most easterly point of land known as "West" Quoddy Light? Like many things in this part of the world, the answer is rooted in maritime history. The site marks the western entrance to an area known as Quoddy Roads through a channel between the United States mainland and Campobello Island in Canada. The first lighthouse was built here in 1808, and replaced with the current 48-foot tower in 1858.

The red and white stripes reflect a Canadian influence and are intended to make the tower stand out against snow during the winter months.

Today, the grounds of the lighthouse are part of Quoddy Head State Park and feature trails that trace a line between the ocean and the forest—a forest that stretches west for nearly 400 unbroken miles. The park is open seasonally from May 15 to October 15.

Photo by: Jerry & Marcy Monkman/EcoPhotography.com

Eggemoggin Textile Studio

Gorgeous blueberry fields overlooking Eggemoggin Reach greet visitors to Christine Leith's textile studio. Inside, three looms and a library of textile books await, in addition to sumptuous handwoven scarves, shawls, capes, and handspun yarns. She

weaves primarily with silk, wool, and alpaca-dyed fiber before going onto the loom.

Open June–August: Tuesday–Saturday 11 am–5 pm.

207-359-5083
6490 Reach Road
(Route 175), Sedgwick, ME
www.chrisleithstudio.com

 studio
workshop

 craft
marketplace

 special
attraction

Wild for Blueberries

If you love blueberry muffins, blueberry pancakes, blueberry pie, or just plain blueberries, chances are you've tasted wild blueberries from Downeast Maine.

One of only four fruit crops native to North America, the wild blueberry has been a part of local culture here for centuries. Today, Maine is the largest producer of wild blueberries in the world, and is responsible for 25 percent of the total blueberry production in North America. Most of the state's 60,000 acres of blueberry fields, or barrens as they are known locally, are located Downeast. Some fields stretch for miles.

Each year during the Machias Wild Blueberry Festival, the town's population swells from 2,400 to more than 15,000 as people from all over come to celebrate and sample the tiny but flavorful fruit. Watch for roadside stands where you can purchase fresh berries, or try out a blueberry rake at a local pick-your-own site.

 lodging   restaurant   artist gallery

Clay Forms Pottery

Visitors will find a group of small buildings connected by paths and gardens on an acre of spruce woods. Signs will lead the way to this gallery for an assortment of handmade functional and decorative porcelain made by Melody Lewis-Kane.

Open daily,
June–October 9 am–6 pm.

207-359-2320
Rope Ferry Road
Sedgwick, ME
www.clayformspottery.com

North Country Textiles

Color and comfort are the catchwords here. This studio is located in the Levy House blending history with more than three decades of innovative handwoven design. Plush blankets, cushy throws, and eye-catching scarves are made by local weavers. Looms in the shop are set up for demonstrations. In addition to textiles, the store carries pottery, jewelry, and fused glass made by Maine artisans.

Open year-round, hours vary according to season.
Call or check web site for details.
Partially Handicapped Accessible.

207-374-2715 • Levy House, Main Street, Blue Hill, ME
www.northcountrytextiles.com

Handworks Gallery

Colors abound in this collection of contemporary crafts and fine art by Maine artists, featuring woven rugs, floor cloths, wall hangings, paintings, jewelry, art to wear, as well as functional and sculptural works in clay, wood, stone, and glass.

Open May–December:
Monday–Saturday 10 am–5 pm.

207-374-5613 • 48 Main Street, Blue Hill, ME
handworks@hypernet.com

 studio
workshop

 craft
marketplace

 special
attraction

The George B. Dorr Museum of Natural History

This Museum investigates, interprets, and displays the natural world of Maine through exhibits produced by College of the Atlantic students. The original headquarters of Acadia National Park has been renovated and expanded to provide a unique site for these exhibitions, programs, and activities.

Open daily
mid-June–Labor Day.
Labor Day–Columbus Day:
Friday–Sunday 1 pm–4 pm,
Saturday 10 am–4 pm.
Monday–Saturday 10 am–5 pm.
Adults $3.50, seniors $2.50, teens $1.50, children $1.00, under 3 free.

207-288-5395 • 105 Eden Street, Bar Harbor, ME
www.coamuseum.org

Native American Festival and Maine Indian Basketmakers Market

Since 1988, this annual festival has been the largest gathering of traditional Wabanaki artisans in Maine. Festival-goers will be enchanted by craft demonstrations, music, story-telling, and dance in celebratation of the heritage of the Penobscot, Passamaquoddy, Micmac, and Maliseet tribes. The festival is sponsored by the Maine Indian Basketmakers Alliance, the Abbe Museum and the College of the Atlantic.

Annually first Saturday after the 4th of July 10 am–4 pm.

207-288-3519 • 105 Eden Street (Route 3) College of the Atlantic, Bar Harbor, ME
www.abbemuseum.org

 lodging   restaurant   artist gallery

Abbe Museum

The Abbe Museum celebrates Maine's Native American heritage through the enduring art and craft traditions of the Wabanaki people, comprising four tribes: Passamaquoddy, Penobscot, Micmac, and Maliseet. Exhibitions showcase Wabanaki crafts, such as ash splint and sweetgrass basketry and wood carvings. Visit either the seasonal, historic museum that opened in 1928 in Acadia National Park or the year-round museum that opened in 2001 in downtown Bar Harbor.

Downtown location: daily late May–late October 9 am–5 pm. Late October–late May: Thursday–Sunday 9 am–5 pm. Closed January. Fee.

Sieur de Monts Spring location: late May–late October: 9 am–4 pm. Limited access.

207-288-3519 · 26 Mount Desert Street (2nd location: Sieur de Monts Spring), Bar Harbor, ME · www.abbemuseum.org

Island Artisans/Island Designs, Bar Harbor

Don't miss Bar Harbor's most complete selection of quality arts and crafts by over 75 of Maine's leading artisans, featuring creations in textiles, pottery, baskets, paper, wood, jewelry, glass, silver, stone, and metal. Members and owners Chong and Judi Lim of Island Designs make embossed and handmade paper, using images that are highly representational, sometimes bordering on surreal, with a style between Eastern and Western. Visitors will find out why the beauty of the natural surroundings inspires the work of the artisans in this shop.

Open daily
May–October,
November–December:
Friday–Saturday.

207-288-4214
99 Main Street,
Bar Harbor, ME
www.islandartisans.com

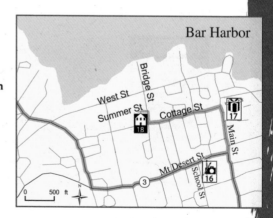

Bar Harbor

 studio workshop

 craft marketplace

 special attraction

247

Black Friar Inn

Surrounded by a perennial flower garden, this Inn is on a quiet side street in Bar Harbor, a short walk to restaurants,

shops and the ocean with Acadia National Park one mile away. Guests will understand why it was voted Arrington's 2002 Bed and Breakfast with the friendliest Innkeepers and Pam Lanler's 1999 Inn of the Year.

Open May–November.

207-288-5091 • 10 Summer Street, Bar Harbor, ME
www.blackfriarinn.com

 ## Lunaform

Phil Lawless and Dan Farrenkopf's outsized vision finds a home among the rocks and cliffs of the coastline. Not only are the garden containers— urns and fountains—timeless in their form, but are built to withstand the elements. All pieces are hand turned, steel-reinforced concrete in a variety of natural color and textural finishes.

Open Monday–Friday 9 am–5 pm, call ahead.

207-422-0923 • 66 Cedar Lane, Sullivan, ME
www.lunaform.com

 ## Hog Bay Pottery/Susanne Grosjean Rugs

Earth, wind, and fire are the elements in Charles and Susanne Grosjean's studio situated near a tidal marsh. The

pottery—dinnerware, casseroles, and lamps—is functional high-fired or wood-fired stoneware. Visitors can find handwoven area rugs made with strong geometric patterns and rich colors using hand spun and hand dyed, local wool.

Open daily May–October 9 am–4 pm.

207-565-2282
245 Hog Bay Road, Franklin, ME
www.hogbay.com

Suzanne Grosjean rug

 lodging   restaurant   artist gallery

Spring Woods Gallery

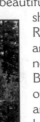

Let yourself be led into this charming two-story gallery in a wooded setting surrounded by beautiful landscaping and shaded gardens. Rocky coastal scenes are rendered by noted illustrator Paul Breeden. Oil paintings of endearing animals and pets are created by popular artist Ann Breeden. Visitors can find a wide selection of signed prints, including botanical plates and limited edition wildlife prints, as well as a unique collection of handmade cards featuring the Breeden's art and photography.

Open May–October: Monday–Saturday 9 am–5 pm, Sunday by chance.

207-422-3007 · 19 Willowbrook Lane, Sullivan, ME
www.springwoodsgallery.com

Proper Clay Stoneware at Stave Island Gallery

Susan Dickson-Smith's gallery is in a cedar-shingled cottage next to an 1880s farmhouse, surrounded by gardens, pink granite ledges, and acres of forest. The gallery sits beside a pond, home to countless frogs and a favorite stop for herons and ducks. "I make hand-thrown functional stoneware pottery, inspired by the forms and colors of Maine sea, sky and stone. After each piece is thrown on the potter's wheel, I often enhance the form through carving, faceting or paddling the pot. The work is then fired, stained and glazed, and fired again."

Open June–October: Tuesday–Saturday 9 am–5 pm or by appointment.

207-963-2040 · 636 South Gouldsboro Road (Rt. 186), Gouldsboro, ME
www.properclay.com

Proper Clay Stoneware vase

 studio workshop
 craft marketplace
 special attraction

Mama's Boy Bistro

Watch the water while feasting on fine, locally-grown, organic food, artfully served. Visitors will discover a welcome respite for evening meals.

Open March–September: Tuesday–Sunday 5 pm–9 pm.

207-963-2365
10 Newman Street,
Winter Harbor, ME
www.mamasboy.com

U.S. Bells

The beautiful Schoodic Peninsula beckons, and is answered with bells! Richard Fisher pours bronze in his working foundry

to cast original wind and door bells. He also creates coat racks, plant stands, and bronze hardware. Most of the designs, especially the wind bells, are unique and contemporary, while other designs are inspired by traditional Shaker hardware or ship bells. Pottery, paintings, and woodcarving by local artisans are also featured.

Open April–October:
Monday–Friday 9 am–5 pm,
Saturday 9 am–2 pm. Call off season.
Partially Handicapped Accessible.

207-963-7184 • 866-963-7184
56 West Bay Road, Prospect Harbor, ME • www.usbells.com

 lodging   restaurant artist gallery

Wild Blueberry Land

This one-of-a-kind, blueberry-shaped blueberry shop features blueberry candy, blueberry pies, blueberry jellies and jams, blueberry pie filling, blueberry ceramic ware, and many more products made from locally grown wild blueberries. Other products include handmade soaps, candles, kitchenware, walking sticks, and Native American jewelry, and more.

Open year-round. Check ahead for hours.

US Route 1, Columbia Falls, ME
www.wildblueberryland.com

DownEast Drawings & Wildlife Art Gallery

Award-winning artists, Fred and Patty Hartman, invite visitors to their gallery and studio along a tidal stream surrounded by forest and fields. The gallery contains original drawings and prints of Maine landscapes and wildlife gracefully rendered in pen and ink, watercolor, pencil, and pastel. There is also a large selection of note-cards, note-pads, mugs, cookbooks and other useful items decorated with signature downeast attractions and local landscapes.

Open year-round. Almost always there, but please call ahead.

207-733-0988 · Rt. 189, Whiting, ME
dnestdrw@localnet.com

Bold Coast Smokehouse

Vinny and Holly Gartmayer cater across the country with their mouth-watering smoked salmon, halibut, mackerel, and "whatever else we can smoke up by the time you get here!" They also prepare handcrafted patés with the freshest fish this side of Halifax.

Open daily 8 am–5 pm.

207-733-8912 · Rte 189, Lubec, ME
www.boldcoastsmokehouse.com

 studio workshop

 craft marketplace

 special attraction

Raye's Mustard Mill

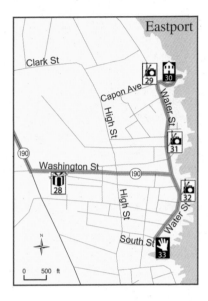

28

Don't miss this mouth-watering stop to the country's last stone mustard mill! In 1900, J.W. "Wes" Raye, whose father captained coastal schooners on the Bay of Fundy, set up his first mill in the family smokehouse to grind mustard sauces for the growing sardine industry. Ever since, this working museum has crafted award-winning mustards 100% stone ground from whole seeds. The Pantry Store features a broad range of regional arts, crafts, and foods.

Open June–December: Monday–Friday 8 am–5 pm, Weekends 10 am–4 pm. January–May: Monday–Friday 9 am–4 pm, Saturday 10 am–4 pm. Tours on the hour between 10 and 3 on weekdays and some Saturdays.

207-853-4451 • 800-853-1903
83 Washington Street, Eastport, ME • www.rayesmustard.com

Leister Gallery

29

A fine art gallery of representational paintings by David and Martha Leister. David paints landscapes and seascapes with oil and watercolor. Martha's mediums of choice are oil and pastel for creating landscapes, seascapes, still life, and portraits.

Visitors can find reproduction greeting cards of their paintings.

Open July–September 10 am–5 pm or by appointment.

207-853-2319
153 Water Street, Eastport, ME
www.leistergallery.com

🏠 lodging   🍴 restaurant   📷 artist gallery

Todd House Bed and Breakfast

This full cape built around a cabin has three historic notables: it is shown on a 1763 map drawn for the British Admirality before the American Revolution; men met in the house in 1801 to form a Masonic Order; and the house was billeted during the Civil War to provide shelter for soldiers. Visitors can stay a night or just take a house tour to view the many period pieces in use. Children and pets are welcome.

Open year-round.

207-853-2328 · 1 Capen Avenue, Todd's Head, Eastport, ME

The Salem Gallery

Artists Jim Salem and Dan Cocco show a variety of acrylic on canvas paintings, ranging from regional realism to contemporary and still life. Visitors can take workshops or wander the beautiful gardens.

Open daily June–mid-Oct. 10 am–6 pm.

**207-853-2454
305-744-9880
120 Water Street,
Eastport, ME
www.jimsalemart.com**

The Salem Gallery

Eastport Gallery

This co-operative gallery represents thirty local artists, including painters, sculptors, and photographers. The phrase "creative diversity" comes to mind in describing the

representational to abstract work. Visitors can find original pieces and reproductions.

Open daily June–October.

**207-853-4166 in season
207-853-0706 off season
52 Water Street, Eastport, ME
www.eastportgallery.com**

 studio workshop

 craft marketplace

 special attraction

253

CROW TRACKS Woodcarving Gallery

33

This gallery features the art of Roland LaVallee, who carries on the Maine tradition of wildlife carvings. The variety and detail of these finely crafted representations make his studio a fascinating place to visit.

Open daily April– December: 9 am–5 pm. October–January: daily 10:30 am–5 pm.

**207-853-2336
11 Water Street,
Eastport, ME
www.crowtracks.com**

Katie's on the Cove/Handmade Confections

34

You can't miss the bright yellow, gaily flowered, chocolate shop on Mill Cove. Using recipes from downeast candymakers of the past, Joseph and Lea lovingly combine only the freshest and finest ingredients to recreate traditional favorites like Maine Potato Candy or Oxhearts. Each confection is patiently perfected to the absolute height of flavor and quality, then hand-formed and hand-dipped. The truffles have been chosen as "best in the state" by *Yankee Magazine's Travel Guide to New England*.

Open June–August: Tuesday–Sunday 10 am–5:30 pm.
May, September: Tuesday, Thursday, Saturday 11 am–5 pm.

**207-454-3297 • 9 Katie Lane, Robbinston, ME
www.katiesonthecove.com**

 lodging   restaurant   artist gallery

Downeast Heritage Museum & Gift Shop

This stunning new facility on the scenic banks of the St. Croix River offers exceptional interpretive exhibits exploring Native American culture, early European settlement in Downeast Maine, and the natural resources to be found in the ocean waters and forest lands that define the region. The gift shop features handmade products by local artist and craftspeople.

Open daily Memorial Day–Columbus Day, 10 am–6 pm, winter hours by appointment and for events.

877-454-2500 · 207-454-7878 · 39 Union Street, Calais, ME
www.downeastheritage.org

Shamel Boat & Canoe Works

Bill Shamel builds cedar canvas, square stern and double-end canoes in his shop. Visitors can watch the process of repairing and restoring wooden canoes and small boats. Also an instructor at the Wooden Boat School, Bill teaches workshops in canoe building and repair in his studio.

Open Monday–Saturday 7:30 am–5 pm.

207-796-8199
42 Tough End Road,
Grand Lake Stream, ME
shamel@midmaine.com

 studio workshop

 craft marketplace

 special attraction

Maine

New Hampshire

New York

Vermont

Key Word Index: Antiques

The Northern Forest Center

The Northern Forest Center was founded in 1997 to mobilize people to build healthy communities, economies and ecosystems by working together across the Northern Forest region. Since then, the Center has conducted research, produced publications, developed programs and convened dialogue and regional exchanges on issues ranging from heritage and culture to economic development, conservation and place-based education.

Working with partners across the four states and across many disciplines, the Center delivers programs and services at three levels:

<u>Local Community Programs</u> to engage residents and communities in the Northern Forest in building regional identity, supporting locally based education and strengthening communities to give the region's youth a reason to stay.

<u>Regional Economy Programs</u> to improve economic and social sustainability to complement the region's great progress in land conservation.

<u>National Policy Programs</u> to develop a national policy agenda to better meet the social and economic needs of the Northern Forest, including increased appropriations and new policy initiatives that benefit the region.

www.northernforest.org

 # Businesses for the Northern Forest

The purpose of Businesses for the Northern Forest is to strengthen long-term business opportunities in the Northern Forest by helping businesses work together to improve the financial, social, and environmental well-being of the region.

The program's goals are to:

Enable businesses in the Northern Forest to connect with each other to improve business opportunities and to contribute to the

262

economic, social, and environmental well-being of the region;

Research and provide information about issues, projects, and activities affecting the economic, social, and environmental well-being of the Northern Forest; and

Support joint activities including communication, marketing, and policy to improve the economic, social, and environmental well being of the Northern Forest and to improve business opportunities.

www.businessnorthernforest.org

HandMade in the Northern Forest is printed on 100% recycled paper.

NEW LEAF
PAPER

Environmental Benefits Statement

This project is printed on New Leaf Opaque 100 made with 100% post-consumer waste and processed chlorine free. Using this environmental paper saved the following resources:

107 Trees

5,127 Pounds of Solid Waste

45,851 Gallons of Water

77 Million BTUs of Energy

10,001 Pounds of Greenhouse Gases

21 Pounds of Air Emission
(HAPs, VOCs, TRSs combined)

257 Pounds of Hazardous Effluent
(BODs, TSSs, CODs, AOXs combined)

Calculation based on research by Environmental Defense and other members of the Paper Task Force.

For more information on this environmental benefits statement, or to inquire about environmentally friendly papers, please contact New Leaf Paper - info@newleafpaper.com - 888-989-5323.

Notes